CALL IT FORTH

POEMS, STORIES & COLUMNS

by Dasha Kelly

Produced by
Mpact Communications
300 W. Walnut St.
Milwaukee, WI 53212

Author photography by
Karama Sadaka (New York)

DashaKelly.com

Poems

STORIES

COLUMNS

MICRO BLOGS
(commonly known as "status updates")

for **DAPHNE**

THANK YOU, MAMA, FOR
TEACHING ME TO
COUNT STARS.

SPARE CHANGE

At the edge of the bed
Watching you sleep
Counting, again, your shiny pieces
Charting the haphazard precision
of our journeys
Marveling at the perfection of God

FORECAST

He said
We all carry a storm inside
He spoke to no one in particular
Everyone at once
We were gathered in polite distances
Tempests spinning in our chests

Our conversations were a symphony of
thunderclaps and howl
Electricity and torrent
We trade glances, opaque
with glacial cold and slow
molten gurgles of stone

We are ravaged by wind and wishing
Sand and secrets
Broad acreages of intention and expectations
Devastated by unrelenting rains
We are littered with fallen trees and debris
Relief may never come
Maybe came and went
Some will adapt to this rubble
Some have already perished in
depths of apocalyptic rains

We all carry a storm inside
Rainbow dreaming
for a new, clear day

Moon

Pocked with history
and collision debris
She is gorgeous
Luminescent against the darkness
albeit borrowed light
She projects no airs
Bares her scarred surfaces
Wars, she knows, are for stars with
fire left kindling in their bellies
She has long forgotten the cool nights
spent racing between planes
Bending space, flirting with time
Her course is fixed in the sky now
Adventure and whimsy
crumbling away like stale gossip
Her crooked smile once beguiled
romantic young scholars
She remembers when her seduction
was more legend than lore

From her distance
she sings a night song
Satisfied to still
lure the sea

BRAT

I'm from airport terminals and
packing tape
Vaccination shots and
passport stamps
I'm from swallowing goodbyes and
grinding new language inside my cheek

New school rules
New kid blues
I'm from counting backwards
Years, months, weeks and days
to start again

I'm from stiff salutes
Uniforms and fatigues
Rush hour cars stalled in their places
for flags at half mast
for the playing of *Taps*

I'm from sacrifice and tongue biting
Big words and small miracles

I am from Nowhere, USA

VESSEL

Don't mind this vessel
This fragile deceit
This body

I carry the constellations on my shoulder blades
Ocean lava on my tongue
Do not mind this vessel
Modest and out of balance
with the landscape

You are not native to these hills
to their humble grandeur chiseled
from quartz and feldspar
Clear water and sunshine spill from my wounds

Don't mind the fractures between these plates
or the gloss of my heavy stones
I carry gale storms inside my palms
Carry us both across mocking canyons
to wild flower thatches

Don't speculate the might of this vessel
This wrapping of flesh and purpose
A universe endeavors beneath my skin
my container
my painted earthenware

Do not
underestimate
me

I pray for the serenity to accept the things I cannot change, the courage to change the things I can, and the wisdom to know when to pitch a #$!@% hissyfit anyway...

Here's a SHEcret: fellas, you might not be included in her -ahem- "headcount." She won't flat out deny that you happened (maybe), but you're not making the tally report. Why? Lots of reasons: she was already close to quota or it was only a partial package or, maybe, you were just really bad. Anyhoo, just thought you'd want to know. Good luck!

When your reputation precedes you (and there will come a time...), will people expect the best or worst when You actually show up? Let's keep working on that, ya...?

Checked Google and WebMD. Apparently this curious affliction is called "sleepy."

WORDS

I'm not sure when it happened, when my words fell away from ordinary, peeling away sneakers to don ruby slippers, requesting lemon zest and garnish. I don't know, exactly, when my words were made to hang back in the green room waiting for a green light to shine.

My words didn't think twice about being seen without makeup, in sweatshirts and jeans. They miss racing one another down to sheets of paper, squealing and breathless until they tumble and fall into unexpected formations. My words spend too much time standing around these days, clustered into genres, waiting for invitations to arrive. They are social creatures but miss their quiet time, too. My words need to sprawl across clean pages, even find themselves crumpled and tossed away sometimes. They are not all destined for posterity, but each marks a heartbeat in this world.

My words don't mind posing in display cases or smiling into a lens, but they are weary of being thrown into dance routines and cinched at the waist with corsets. They don't need office hours or handlers, Egyptian cotton or candy dishes picked free of green M&Ms. My words don't need whole bean coffee or fair trade chocolate or chicken wings with six exotic sauces.

My words remember the landscape before our ideas got gentrified. They are homesick for meandering, deadline -free afternoons. My words know that they are loved. They are unfamiliar with fear, but recognize its acrid fumes. They are commissioned, each and every one, to soldier gruesome conflicts. My words are complex in their simplicity. Graceful in their strength. Unassuming in their power.

They are unafraid of expectation, and not guaranteed to assemble themselves into solutions. My words know how to be silly. Foolish. Haughty. Wicked. Even raunchy. My words do not always behave.

They don't require reason or rhyme, just space. Not a stage or a two page spread, just space. Whether they file into dense and determined rows or pirouette into limber arcs, they only need space so they can breathe. My words only want to breathe. Breathe. Breathe. Breathe.

They're just words. Letters bonding into cliques. Sentences falling into flash mob formations. Paragraphs pledging solidarity on the page. And they have always been the boss of me.

I've been held together by words, pulling them into me like breath, since I was 10. Although I don't suspect many of my elementary school classmates were also spending their summers with a typewriter, it wasn't until college that I recognized writing as a gift and not an innate skill. Back then, my attachment to writing was merely affection. Writing professionally had never, not once ever, crossed my mind. I was double-majoring in Corner Office and Fat Rolodex and had absolutely no frame of reference for the absurd notion of pursuing a committed relationship with my words.

I still scribbled stories. They were a mental release from project papers, my way to relax. Through graduation and into the adult world, writing persisted as a hobby I liked to keep handy, right next to the deck of playing cards, watercolor brushes and beat-up Scrabble board.

In my day-to-day conversations, however, my passion for words — those sexy and sublime words — blazed at the world, fiery and blatant. I'd spent so many years feeling misunderstood as a kid (perhaps the summers with the typewriter didn't help) that framing myself and my thoughts in clarifying metaphors and analogies became second nature. Digging into my vocabulary became an exercise in precision, not pretention. Once, on a date, I was in the middle of what I thought was a hilarious and riveting story when he interrupted to ask the definition of "conniption."

"It means having a fit," I said.

After a frustrated pause, he asked, "So why didn't you just say 'having a fit'?"

I tried to explain how conniption's hard consonant was suited for the compound sentence, about the rhythm of its clipped second syllable, how the word prompted you to prepare for a turn in the story. Of course, I didn't have any of this language. I could only insist that "conniption" worked better. Subsequently, he could only presume that I was an ass.

Somewhere along the way, my private affair with writing went public. Words escaped the tower of my imagination, shimmying down to find their way into books, onto computer screens and in front of live audiences. From sharing one story with one friend nearly 20 years ago, I now find myself compelled to share all of my best work with the planet.

Ignorance, however, is truly a delicious kind of bliss.

Since committing to my words and answering to the title "writer," I haven't approached my words with the same ease. When I simply had a crush on them, I could sit at the computer and devote an entire afternoon to a story that was only destined for a file folder. I could pick up my journal and find epiphanies through poems that would never meet printer's ink or a microphone.

In boldly parading our union to the world, I find myself pressing my words through unforgiving filters. Partly, it's the reality of paying bills, raising children, and consuming more leafy greens that makes me so discerning about the time I allow for writing. Partly, it's the humility in knowing that lightning bolts in the shape of publishing contracts might never strike. Mostly, I'm guilty of objectifying my words, of only spending quality time when there's someplace special for us to go. Long ago, when I didn't know any better and no one knew about my words, things were different. Organic. Easy.

A dear friend once confided in me about challenges he was facing in his new marriage. He and his wife had shared an incredible connection when they were dating so I was surprised to learn they were struggling as newly-weds. Their breakthrough happened, he said, when his wife turned off the movie they were watching and told him to leave the house. She demanded that he meet his boys at the bar, like he used to. Stay out until the wee hours that night, like he used to. Come home to consume her with gluttony and abandon, like he used to.

"I thought being a husband meant I wasn't sup-posed to go out with the fellas anymore or get pissy drunk or pull her hair during sex," he said. "There are new rules for all that, but I realized I was trying to live a title in-stead of living my life."

I think of them these days, ticking off more than a dozen wedding anniversaries by now. I, too, have allowed a title to commandeer the relationship with my writing. Now that we're official, and consummating concerns about submissions, commissions, agents, queries, and such, it's like I don't know how to love on my words the way I used to. It's like I'm afraid to mess up something I've been doing my entire life.

I need to balance the work of being a writer with the whimsy I remember. My intelligent self understands that everything I write won't produce a paycheck, an op-portunity, or applause. My spirit yearns to sink guiltlessly into that scrumptious in-between space, where stories and poems are simply a byproduct of the sheer love for writing.

My words have always shown up for me, and I am committed to return myself to a space where I can show up with the same selflessness. Yes, in the grand scheme of poverty, intolerance, food deserts, and roving the surface of Mars, these are *just* words. But I owe them so much more than that.

I'd make a pitiful hostage.

FB STATUS :: FEB 21 2013

AfriCobra

Pigments burst brilliant
Coil fiercely around semantics
around freedom
around blackness
around all we have been

Truth as skeleton, as skin
Pain as skeleton, as skin
Power as skeleton as pain as
truth as blackness as we
always have been

Colors extracted from the universe
smear prophecy in hues of clay,
harvest, gemstone, sunrise
Pigments burst brilliant through midnight sky
through shadow
through darkness
through wicked

Clay. Harvest. Gemstone. Sunrise.
Soul colors shape
our silhouette into a new day

HISTORY

He had a job collecting insurance payments, $2 a week
Drove a covered wagon to El Dorado
searching for gold
Died in the mines there
Poured wine on the Titanic
Ate dinner with DuBois
(One time)
Forced the bank to open a checking account,
separate from her husband's
Cleaned the tiger cage on the circus train
Cleaned a whorehouse near Reno
Helped clean up the city after Katrina
Fell 40 floors from the new scaffolding of Chicago
Contracted polio
Lived near the internment camps and
swore she heard them screaming
Worked the lights in *Birth of a Nation*
Worked at CJ Walker's factory
Scheduled to work the day of Apollo XI, but
his appendix burst
Burst through the banner at the Rose Bowl
Crossed the border without her family
Passed through Ellis Island without his wife
Refused to cut his hair
Refused to burn her bra
Was charged with war crimes
heresy
tax evasion
Hammered wet metal into missiles
Posted the bill of sales for slaves
Showed housewives how to sell Tupperware
War
God
Dope
Taught blind children to read with their fingers

Hung laundry on the line before
Harlem changed hands
Haight Ashbury
Bronzeville
Raised babies filled with lead
Filled with music
Convinced the neighbors to mount their
speakers in the windows
Challenged the union to overlook her breasts
Overlook his boyfriend
The crooked angles of their legs
Prepared notes for Dr. King
Repaired a trumpet for Miles Davis
Signed warrants for the Salem witch trials
Enlisted in the service
Registered for nursing school
Ran moonshine
Collected shot glasses from all around the world
Always made pies for the bake sales
Never came home for Christmas
Died on Mama's birthday
Threw the first rock of Red Summer
Threw the switch on death row
Threw Junior out of the house
Saved a man's life
on the subway one day
Mailed his last dollar to help
build the Statue of Liberty,
Little red school house
Memorized all of Chuck Berry's moves
Kennedy's speeches
Grandma's recipes
Bet against Joe Louis
Made love to Doc Holliday
the deacon and the pastor
Bruce Lee
El Che
Jimi Hendrix
Planted the first orange trees in the city

Was the first girl to wrestle in the district
First altar boy to break their silence
Never told a soul about the operation
Never responded to the summons
Never stopped going to auditions
Never came back to town
Stayed sober
Stayed together
Stayed angry until they died
Kept a vigil
Kept the faith
Kept a locket to remember

Remember

You will be remembered inside of these
intricate histories by someone

Or maybe no one will recall
that scar on your face

But your story cannot be erased
Your heartbeat is a forever history

Forever
History
You. Were. Here.

INCANTATION No. 1

The floor lamp in my kitchen is sleek,
sturdy, brilliant and fickle.
To coax light from its bulb, I grip
the post and give it a full shake.

My favorite bracelet is patterned
with black stones. Two are missing.
I wear it anyway, aligning the empty
spaces with the tattoo of my veins.

I can remotely activate my house alarm
with a fob on my keychain.
It's held together with packaging tape,
a roll I own only because of the box
I shipped to New York last year.
The excess, handy at last.

My cell phone is less smart than most.
I pry open the casing occasionally
to revive its lithium battery
in the palm of my hand.
Nothing under this sun is perfect, but you still
must come to me whole.
Whether held in place with duct tape,
or lost game pieces replaced with bottle tops,
hold out to me all that you are.

Prove yourself aware of your own wiring, and I will
arrive half past the hour, just in time for your solo. Will
taste every sampler chocolate free
from your curious bite. Skip the stubborn refrain
of smudged and scratched music.
I do not desire the limitations of perfection.
Your limp will counter my ache.
I only ask that you come to me whole.

Transform your small deuce into
the biggest trump card. Double
the amount of tarragon or garlic or heavy cream.
Jiggle the handle. Pump the brakes. Hold down
the left side until it opens. Study your manual
appendix. Polish the scuffs. Join me in loving
the contents of these dented containers. Make this
life work, work.

Curled together, our shoulders will slope away
the tonnage of this world. Only if you come to me whole.

STAINLESS STEEL

The confession rolled from under my tongue
Stark, clean
Precise in its movement
away from shadowed recesses
Moved smooth across my language
Something like steel ball bearings
Something like truth

Daughter: So the Netherlands are real.
Me: Huh? What do you mean?
Daughter: I thought it was just in Peter Pan.
Me: *takes a second to process*
That's Never Never Land, girl!!
Daughter: Oh... Don't judge me.

FB STATUS :: DEC 16 2012

I'm reminded not to be too judgmental
when regular people do stupid things
*as I wipe fruit smoothie from the wall after tossing in
one more peach slice...with the lid off*

FB STATUS :: MAY 11 2011

My children, apparently, are big fans of this thing
called "dinner." Every day, even! smh. Crazy
kids...

FB STATUS :: OCT 21 2012

Dynamic. Beautiful. Hard working. A true loss
to the Underwear Drawer community. Safe
passage, Black Satin Bra. Your underwire held
up for as long as it could, but the time has come.
I will miss you; Black Satin Bottoms will miss you;
all the other bras from the clothesline
will miss you, too (yes, even Red Lace).
We shared some good times...

FB STATUS :: MARCH 27 2013

SCRIBE

He aligned his fingers along the bag seam and pulled hard. Even to himself, he seemed to inhale the potato chips rather than chew them.

"Sure would be nice to have some chips in a bag of chips, huh?" he said to his seatmate, but she had already tucked in her ear buds and laid open a magazine across her lap.

He nodded to himself and turned to face the window. She wasn't listening to music. The aircraft was still grounded, so the patrolling attendants continued to ask if her device was turned off. Her response time was too prompt, too aware, he surmised. She was not listening to music; she was planning not to listen to him.

He wondered why she was traveling this afternoon. What waited for her in St. Louis? He imagined her the aspiring corporate type, taking time off for a family visit. Manicure. Tennis bracelet. Thin fabric of a common chain store. No, a family obligation.

He was itching to ask her whether he was on the right track about any of it. Of the woman stuffed into the seat ahead of them, he was certain. Grandmother. Former beauty queen. Salon highlights. Fashion comfortable. Upper lid mascara. The ease in her smile as she jabbered into her phone. He'd taken her in while they were all waiting at the gate.

He could've continued with her biography, but the woman sitting next to him was decidedly inaccessible. Single. Unreligious. Charismatic. He was fidgeting now. He wanted to know.

He tightened his seatbelt during the safety demonstration and raced through the Sky Mall catalog. The attendants began their final cabin check. This time, it was the grey-haired attendant who reached in to tap his seatmate's shoulder, indicating her device. She nodded in acknowledgement and returned promptly to her magazine.

The attendant hesitated before continuing through the aisle. He stole a glance at his seatmate's profile, rounded and freckled. He pressed back against the seatbelt restraining his excitement. As the plane roared toward the heavens, he closed his eyes and began writing her life story.

STRANGERS

We both pull a foot back up to the curb, calculating the narrowed opportunity for dashing across the street. The oncoming cars do not lurch forward. They are less impatient than we. I look quickly to the traffic sign, for the little LED pedestrian guy. He's flashing red. I look back to the traffic, at the headlights pulling ahead, and acquiesce.

"It's not worth it," says the woman who had gauged her traffic-defying potential beside me.

"This would be the night we slip and fall," I say, shaking my head. Cars snake across our intersection.

"That would be an awful way to go," she says.

This strikes me as funny, for some reason. "Yeah," I say. "I'm hoping to give my people a better story to tell at my funeral."

We're both peeling back the beginning of a laugh. Her voice is chiseled, textured. The caliber you wouldn't want firing threats or reprimands.

"I read about an actress who took a bunch of pills, and they found her with her head in the toilet," she said.

"Not in the toilet," I groaned.

"I don't care what people have to say after I'm dead," she said. "It doesn't matter if they know how I died."

"But *you'll* know!" I insist.

She tosses her head back to free a hearty laugh. I've always had good luck with people who surrender to joy this way.

"I'm not used to your Midwest ways," she says after a moment, and turns to demonstrate a processed, static smile. "I'm from the east coast. When everything is wrong, you see it."

I was told once that, elsewhere, waitresses refer to customers' neat nesting of their own dirty plates as The Midwest Stack. We've got congeniality in the bag.

"It's a practiced survival skill," I say.

"The laugh was good," she says. "I've been remodeling."

"One room or everything?" I ask.

The little LED pedestrian guy lights up for us and we step into the intersection. My comrade moves swiftly, clutching books and binders to her body. She stands at about five foot four, with a revolution of graying chestnut spirals bouncing against her shoulders, keeping time with her steps.

She tells me about the broken sewage pipe. The spewing. The contractors. The boxes of everything she owns. She tells me about her unexpected travel to Baltimore and back. Baltimore and back. Her mother is ill. She asks me what I thought about Philadelphia when I visited.

I describe the sharp contrasts of neighborhoods, the cantina with an octopus on the patio roof, the Gil Scott Heron performance, the unplanned beauty of it all.

We've walked a little more than a block before reaching the Overture. She's in the middle of telling me about online dating. I interrupt.

"I'm heading in here," I say, wanting to hear the end.

"I am too, but it's the other door," she says. We keep walking. She picks up the end of her Match.com story. "So they told me that even if I'm telling the guy 'no thank you,' their computer adds the reply to its algorithm and sends more just like him! So, don't be too nice. That's what I learned."

It's my turn to laugh.

I tell her about my online profile. My divorce. My

writing. My youth program. The show I'm attending. She's heading to the literary revision panel. We both think of staying in touch but pull back our feet. So many invitations evaporate once the moment passes. My mother calls it "vacation promises": they seem real on the horseback ride along the beach but unlikely once you're back in your real life, loading groceries in the trunk.

I go for it anyway and hand her a card. I'm not in the city often, but when I am I'd enjoy a leisurely coffee and conversation with this lively woman. Our not-near-death exchange felt purposed, somehow. Lucky.

"Oh, good!" she says. She's genuine and enthusiastic. "Email me whenever you like. I'll email you back."

Honorary Fellow, Department of Comparative Literature, University of Wisconsin.

The universe is, once again, impressive. Just last week I was advised [read: threatened] by a close friend to start scouting fellowships. I had nodded, though I wasn't convinced I could. Or should.

Lucky, in the divine sense.

I part ways with my curbside compadre, both of us wishing the other a great event. I took to the stairs, no hesitation in my steps. Smiling at the gift in talking to strangers.

I know I'm not the first, last, or even the most
hardscrabble person trying to make it all happen
--laundry, dinner, bills, waistline, dreaming,
permission slips, tweets, kisses, oil changes,
recycling, email, birthday cards... I know. I'm not
alone. Still, some days, I want confetti.
Or maybe a small parade.

FB STATUS :: JULY 25 2013

Dude: You ask really good questions.
I like the way your brain works.
Me: Thanks. Makes dating tough, though.
Dude: *pause* Hmm, I bet.
(Not sure whether to giggle or weep...)

FB STATUS :: NOV 26 2012

Gather your stuff before making a grand exit.
Just had to slink back in for my cell phone.
Ruined everything. Ugh.

FB STATUS :: FEB 19 2010

I wonder what happens if you cuss inside a
prayer. Does an angel get a leather halo or
metal studs on their wings?

FB STATUS :: AUG 30 2010

ANY DAY NOW

Midnight stills his tongue, prayers
snared between his teeth

Death is sauntering through the shadows
patiently waiting to claim its bounty

He knows her time has come, surrenders
their memories to grieving

Fighting is done, she will lay her frail
fingers in Death's outstretched hands

He collects each new sun in his pocket, currency
he saves to measure their final days

Nightfall renders him silent, listening
for her goodbye to erupt in the dark

PINK

Shoulders cloaked in holy
Glad she decided on pink today
On the foreign staccato music
of her high heels clacking the concrete

Pink fuchsia shoes, size 8
Like the dress she wore
with the shoulders out
with her guard down
Appraising eyes, framed by fresh wrinkles
remember her confirmation, her
pageant wings, her baptismal waters

Someone hands her a baby
A bundle of lace and ribbons
cooing melodies of springtime
She bounces and rocks
Hopes her muscles will recall this sliver of grace
when defeat returns to lunge at her face
Smear the coral lipstick from her mouth
Snatch pins from her upswept hair

She returns the baby and stands
on the second church step
A breeze catches her hem
Lifts the auburn strands from her face
Lessons scrubbed harsh against her skin
The wrinkled elders and God
smiled on her like a gift wrapped in fuchsia

Her face points to the sunshine
braving redemption in her smile
She was glad she decided to wear pink today

COUGAR

Lazing beneath
freshly peeled sunshine
She feeds
Corded meat of tender lovers
still sweet in her molars

She climbs from her comfort
Sauntering vengeance through the village,
between shadows,
in broad daylight

She licks the scent of prey out of the wind
a growl motoring in her throat
The length of her tail curls questions in the dirt
She pads gracefully along the horizon

Evolved from dust, brush and scorching judgment
Her belly is full
The taste of a sister's distant kill
weaves itself into the night

Don't get it twisted: there's a pair of big
brass ones beneath this skirt.

FB STATUS :: SEPT 5 2012

GHOST SHIP

Ripped from the edge of the ocean
A knot of steel and fate
flung into the future
Swaddled by a storm
Possessed by the wind
Death compressed into this ghost ship
Carving into icy waters its memorial
of souls we lost to the sea

Canons crumpled 400 feet of iron into a ball
Cracked the fisherman's rig
Sunk it to murky depths
Adding our secrets in piles
along the fragile crust of Earth

MOMENTS AGO AND AGAIN

We settled ourselves around low wooden tables
in a closed drapery of books and
photos of a life well explored

We drew in crinkled air
Took turns unpacking our fairy un-tales
and the Cajun takeout was good
Hand me a napkin
Hand me a lighter
Hand me the hand-dyed
ribbons of your story
We'll tie them each around
our fingers in knotted bows that pop color
and memories
and tethered laughter

Oh I'm sorry, she said into the phone
I didn't hear it ring
I'm sorry, I said
To call so late
She'd told me already
about the woman and the crash and the markers in time
they would both become

I remembered
In that instant
We were different
Pulling speech bubbles out of our cheeks
and from behind our backs
She'd told me already
and I remembered
Moments ago
and later, again,
We were changed

DREAMING

Rainfall drums the windows
Soul music echoes inside
Incense burning
Limbs stretched long and lazy
Tangled beneath heirloom blankets
or a lover
or the heavy lean
of anticipation
Rain will not serenade forever
Right now, close your eyes
and pretend

I don't quite have a Coke bottle figure, but I've
decided that my two-liter is pretty damn fly.

FB STATUS :: MARCH 28 2010

DROPPING CLASSES

Some new syllables pinch
the thick slab of my language
Urging me to remember
Chastising me for not hanging on

Angstrom

These letters might have met me
Had I not dropped Chemistry
Gone on to tackle Physics
with the other honor students in my class
But there's no honor in an F, especially
when you know it's coming

So in ducking science
I dodged Angstrom
The unit of measurement for the length of light rays
One hundred millionth of a centimeter
I missed piercing my tongue
with a word grand enough to
capture infinitesimal wonder

New syllables
easily earning
my reverence

Keep forgetting about the maid.
Mostly, how she doesn't exist.

FB STATUS :: NOV 14 2009

I was on time for EVERYTHING today!! I know,
I know, weeping statues of Mary, Jesus silhouettes in
toast, and now this...

FB STATUS :: MAY 1 2012

See? They didn't know. Oh, sure, they were
convincing when they said you wouldn't survive,
wouldn't amount to much, wouldn't stand up
on your own. But, see? They were wrong.
Okay, fine, you're not everything you said
you'd be either, but...look at you...all alive and making
it work and checking Facebook and shyt...

FB STATUS :: OCT 8 2013

Let me share a few life lessons: 1) don't order fried
chicken at a Chinese restaurant 2) don't use coffee
creamer as a milk substitute in cereal and 3) don't
buy lingerie or panties from the beauty supply store.
This has been a public service announcement ...

FB STATUS :: OCT 7 2009

Co-Conspirator

Published in the blog series during my term
as Narrator for the historic Pfister Hotel.
http://blog.thepfisterhotel.com/author/dasha-kelly

I'm on a stakeout. Granted, I'm not disguised as a delivery person or hiding behind a newspaper. There are no binoculars or dark shades involved. No two-way radio tucked into my sleeve. Although the excitement tickling my gut might suggest that I'm crouched behind a dumpster aiming a telephoto lens, I'm actually perched on a low bench in Blu. It's a handsome crowd and most are here to watch the fireworks. One person is here to rewrite history.

Larry is at a table with his girlfriend, Stephanie. I've known her for a while, but Larry has been like a little brother to me for more than 10 years. About a month ago, he called to ask if I could be on hand when he proposed.

"She's always loved fireworks," he said. "Last summer, I remember turning to look at her and her face was all lit up with lights and she was smiling like a big kid. I remember thinking, 'I absolutely love this woman.'"

Of course, I coo.

"I didn't tell her in that moment, though," Larry said, disappointment laced his words. "I don't know what stopped me. I told her, maybe, the next day. But at the fireworks? Man, that would've been perfect."

The missed opportunity nagged at him. Ready to propose almost a year later, he was determined to create an unforgettable event.

"If I pull this off," he said, "History just might smudge away that fact that I dropped the ball that night, and she'll always associate my 'I love you' with fireworks. Maybe our kids will even retell the story that way."

A conspiracy in the name of love and posterity? I'm in.

I'm at my post, crammed awkwardly between the bar, a married couple to my right and an adult family of six to my left. Everyone faces the window, watching the steel-grey sky surrender to nightfall. I'm making notes in my journal about the crowd, the mood, the floating constellation of lights from boats bobbing n the marina and, of course, Larry and Stephanie. Like many other couples, they're sipping champagne, holding hands, planting kisses, listening to the jazz band, enjoying a romantic evening. I look at my watch.

9:05.

My stomach begins to flutter.

The wait staff hustles to and fro delivering champagne and towers of hors d'ouerves to the tables. When a waiter appears beside him, Larry looks alarmed and I imagine his heart thundering beneath his shirt. He's made arrangements for a custom dessert with "Will You Marry Me" written in chocolate. Not yet. Almost, but not yet.

9:20

The band is back from a mini-break. The singer begins "I Will Always Love You," and the banquet staff approach Larry and Stephanie with their dessert. It takes a moment for its true sweetness to register, and Stephanie begins to smile and giggle. Larry produces the ring box and lowers himself to one knee. I'm not close enough to hear his actual proposal (should've invested in the hidden microphone, after all) but I could hear the whisper rippling around us, "Look, he's proposing!"

Exactly –seriously- exactly as Larry and Stephanie stand to embrace and kiss, the sky erupts in light and

fire. Larry turns to the crowd and confirms, "She said yes!" The entire lounge cheers.

Later that night, I ask Stephanie if she had any idea. She said she had none.

"I called her parents and all of her girlfriends to make sure this went off smoothly," Larry said. "I even made sure that we were dressed up so all the pictures would look nice."

"You really covered your bases," I said. "When did you start planning?"

Larry recounts how he met with her parents early in the year, requested time off from work back in March, started scouting locations in spring, engaged accomplices in early summer, etc. All the while, Stephanie is admiring her ring. Our eyes meet, and she laughs.

"Don't mind me," she says.

"So, how'd he do? I ask.

"This was perfect," Stephanie said, planting another kiss on Larry's cheek. "It was everything, and it was perfect."

Stephanie rested against Larry's arm, smiling up at him as she draped a wrist over his shoulder. We were all silent, indulging in the gaze. The ring dressed her hand beautifully. Stephanie radiated. Larry beamed. The diamonds winked with fire and light. I am still smiling after we hug goodbye and they have head to the elevators. Smiling, and I have no doubt their children will long tell love stories about fireworks.

I suppress a giggle as Daughter 1 rats out Daughter 2 for trying to wear an unauthorized training bra today: "She has to wait for her turn like everybody else..."

FB STATUS :: JAN 8 2010

Been on a major popcorn kick lately (the real deal: kernels, oil and big pot) To my horror, realized that the sight of me "eating" popcorn is actually a violent visual of me shoveling as much popcorn into my face as humanly possible. Fistfuls, really. Stray kernels fall to the floor, down my shirt, in my lap, and I munch away like a happy, oversized chipmunk. Well, I'm not saying I need to change, but I might want to clean this up before accepting any more movie dates.

FB STATUS :: MAY 7 2013

I'd like to return these cooties to their rightful owner.

FB STATUS :: SEPT 27 2011

Yes, clever conversations are included in the standard Me package. Revelations, insights and disclosures sold separately.

FB STATUS :: JULY 5 2013

SNAPSHOTS

She had small features. Skin pulled taut across her face, scarcely disguising the sharp edges of her skull. He felt he should record this image of her. Commit her prim youth to eternity, knowing her wrinkled and silvered self would appear more natural. Pierced by her small, granite eyes people would wonder about her life, about the might implied in her small frame and boned fingers. They would wonder about the old woman. She is yet impressive. Yet.

Googly

we like it when you grab our hair
fingers slide from nape to scalp
cinch tightly around the roots
wrestle with your nature while
hands explore skin landscapes
we like it when you fist feminine curls
into a frenzied knot

despite the propaganda, you should know
we like it when you grab our hair
gather random wild patches
between random wild moments, and hold on
your authority rising to steer, counter,
balance and unleash

tentative at first, hands fan clumsily
fingers slide from nape to scalp
cinch tightly around the roots
your hunger swells beyond social contract
the first tug surprises us both

we sense your muscles shift into hungry concert
wrestle with your nature while
hands explore skin landscapes
meet your inner beast at that moment
ignite a primal impulse to feed

consent escapes from our breeding in hot, muffled moans
we like it when you fist feminine curls
into a frenzied knot
we, too, have beasts prowling our perimeters
we like it when you grab our hair

EIGHTH WONDER INCARNATE

Tis a marvel
how shame glows beneath his skin
Lightening bug
Jellyfish
Atom bomb
Toxic waste, he is.

Tis a marvel
how wicked slicks his tongue
Crude
Sludge
Tar
Snake oil, he is.

Tis a marvel
how his conscience defies gravity
Above reason
Beyond the pale
Inside black holes
Dark matter, he is.

Tis a marvel
how greed fastens to his breathing
Black lungs
Black death
B lack soul
Black plague, he is.

Tis a marvel
how she loves him
Still

ABOUT LEAVING

I only think of leaving you
between the slotted points of morning
Before swinging my feet
from beneath these worn blankets
and forcing my weight onto the floor
I think of leaving you then

Imagine myself rising to greet the sun
from some new horizon
a new mattress
a new walk to brush my teeth
I think of leaving you behind me
then

Tucking away your disappointments and afflictions
like snapshots stuffed into shoe boxes
never destined for a frame
We'd always talk about sorting them out
Pressing labels onto photo album spines, but
supposing is all we've ever been good at
I'm sure we never planned on resenting each other

We wonder what this relationship might be if
I could re-engineer the ambitious wiring
that led me back to you in the first place
If you could engine past the rust and biting decay
I once said gave you your charm

You've probably hoped to find a note one day
An overwritten apology
scratched in my tumbling hand
You might not even read it right away
Breathe out that sigh of relief trapped
behind your cream city bricks
Lie back to let dry stubble,

aluminum cans and refuse consume you
Remind yourself of the others
who will embrace you just the way you are
Won't insist on evolving from
the only way you ever learned how to love:
Conditionally
and without flourish

And I always knew this about you
Didn't settle myself into your spaces
unaware of your history
Unsympathetic to the rugged hands that yanked
and pulled at your upbringing, tragically
convincing you that
this
is all you should strive for

And you knew I've always been different
Coached to peek under the sun for wild imaginings
You've been more successful at being practical
You know better, you said, than to risk singing
the tips of your fingers on the surface of the sun
I tried to show you how beautiful
the scars can be sometimes

I empty my coffee into the sink
Slide on my shoes and my lipstick
Prepare to wrap my face in raw morning sun
I won't think of leaving you then
With your crisp smell slipping familiar into my chest
Your concrete rising to meet my feet
You've always known how I move, even when
you couldn't understand my walk

I don't plan to leave you anytime soon, Milwaukee
I'm still hopeful
we can find more loving to do

While waiting for something amazing to happen to you, go ahead and be something amazing to yourself.

FB STATUS :: MAY 15 2013

With legalization comes taxation and, of course, commercialization. Then what? Brand development, market research, quality control, franchising, event sponsorship, certification classes, closeout sales, gift cards...? The Weed Man might eventually need a toll -free customer service number and a website.

FB STATUS :: JAN 3 2013

Oldest daughter told our cat, Shkoobi, to watch his back. This adds a whole new twist to sibling rivalry

FB STATUS :: SEPT 29 2012

I thought Bin Laden was killed so that I could finally pack skin cream and hair conditioner in my carry-on luggage again. It seems that, perhaps, I misunderstood this whole foreign policy thing...

FB STATUS :: JUNE 4 2011

Graham's eyes slid closed and he lowered his chin to his chest with a small, defeated sigh. He hadn't yet moved his hand from the doorknob. He could still leave. He could say he hadn't heard her when she fussed about it later. He'd been able to slide these smallest of fibs past her before.

Opening his downcast eyes, his attention settled on the door knob and the broad white ribbon looped there. It was from a floral bouquet he'd sent her once. The loops of its elaborate bow hanging down like a wilted blossom.

"Are you still there?" Marissa called. "Graham?"

Her voice smacked his hand from the knob and turned him away from the door that would have released him into the garage. He looked at the scaffolding of dirty dishes in the sink. *Now, Graham,* they mocked. *Later is never better than now.*

The lineup of ceramic sunflower canisters were quiet, filled with their flour, sugar, rice and tea bags. The sunflower wall clock ticked contentedly to itself. Snapshots on the fridge were held in place with round, yellow magnets. Their Vegas trip. Her goddaughter's birthday. Him, with their dog, Jojo. Her, at the bistro after he'd proposed.

"Graham!"

Marissa appeared at the kitchen entrance, hardly filling the passage. It had been these elegant, arched doorways that first held him smitten with their bungalow. He looked at her without speaking.

Her small hands splayed at her sides like baby starfish. "Did you hear me?"

He noticed the ramp in her voice at the end.

"What, you called me?" he asked, satisfying himself with the small lie. "I came back for a Pepsi."

Graham's limbs fumbled against themselves, ambling toward the pictures and yellow magnets. He opened the door and scanned the shelves.

"Get some water," Marissa said.

He looked at the bottles of water glowing in front of the interior bulb. He touched the Pepsi can. He didn't really want it.

"Never mind," he mumbled, the lie remained tangy on his tongue.

Her stony expression liquefied like molten rock into fluttering lashes and pleading eyes. He wouldn't want to do it, whatever the request. He remembered when she wore this face for him always. Fluttering her lashes when she surprised him at work, when she sat cross legged at the café misted all over with floral perfumes, when she perched in his lap and linked her delicate wrists behind his neck.

She had been like a pet bird, small and exotic. She was still a bird, he supposed, just not his pet. She only fluttered for these favors now. He watched her lips spread and pucker, hinge open and closed. All of her words were so rigid now. Wooden blocks tumbling and stacking into her new language. Do this. Do that. Bridal this. Bridal that.

"Do you want me to write it down?" Marissa said, interrupting herself.

"No, I got it," he said, cringing at the thought of carrying one more of her lists.

"You're not listening," her face volcanic rock again.

"I'm listening. I'm standing here, listening," Graham said, parking his clammy hands along his waistband, hoping to look sufficiently annoyed. "Just tell me again so I can get it all. I don't want to be running around all afternoon. I still have to go in to the museum today."

She stilled her arms. Where flailing might signal an emotional storm for most, Marissa willed herself motionless before her downpours. Graham was quiet, not wanting to escalate to her ready tears and find himself trapped in the sunflower kitchen and invariably admit some act of treason to quell her weeping. He would urgently reaffirm his love for her and, yes, emphatically yes, assure her the he really, really wanted to marry her.

Graham wished more than anything, in fact, to

marry Marissa right now to bypass the purgatory of wedding planning.

It was his fault, somehow. He should have known that she would be the breed to change. Undo herself.

"Never in the winter, homie," his brother had said during halftime one Sunday. "You propose in winter, they can't get the reception hall they want for that summer—and they all want a summer wedding so their bridesmaids can have their shoulders out and shit—and the whole thing drags out for a year and *a half.*"

"Would've been nice for my big brother to clue me in before I proposed," Graham had said, glaring at the screen.

"Not my fault you're stupid," his brother had said, shoving his shoulder and handing him a beer.

Graham stepped out into garage. Once in the car, he adjusted the rearview mirror and seat to accommodate his long frame. He wasn't so much tall as he was lanky. His arms and legs folded like hinged yard sticks, the kind his elementary teachers had kept mounted on the chalkboard rack.

He'd stopped asking Marissa to slide back the driver's seat and lower the mirror for him when she explained away her forgetfulness with cake tasting or candelabras. Tuxedo buttons, she said, kept her from washing dishes. Reservation cards stole her attention from their Sunday paper. He pulled from the garage every morning, grateful to escape, even if just for the day.

"Graham, that teacher called back about their field trip."

He turned to face his program manager and said, "What part of 'closed for repairs' is confusing to her?"

Millar smiled and shrugged. She stood at the front counter, arranging exhibit flyers. Her mink hair was swept into a long ponytail across one shoulder. They both wore jeans and a sweater. Even dressed down, Graham thought Millar was stunning. Her complexion, a shade between bisque and burnished sugar, launched strangers into guessing games about her nationality. Moroccan? Egyptian? Peruvian? New Zealander?

"South Carolina Strom Thurmond," she would always say.

Millar looked up from her display and noticed his consuming eye. She asked, "How long is your list this weekend?"

Graham felt his neck warm and he dropped his eyes. He said, "Too damn long, as usual."

Every Second

Published in the blog series during my term as Narrator for the historic Pfister Hotel.
http://blog.thepfisterhotel.com/author/dasha-kelly

"You want to know about Indian culture?" he asks with a raised brow.

I pick up my pen, square my shoulders, and give an affirmative bring-it-on nod.

The lobby lounge is relaxed after a full day of visitors and tourists trafficking through the hotel. I'm having an evening coffee at the bar and my guest, Murali, is unwinding with a glass of whiskey. His flight from India touched down only a few hours ago. He's in the t-shirt business and his work carries him all over the globe: Sri Lanka, Australia, Europe, Japan, Singapore. He's in Milwaukee for the first time.

"I left home for work as a young man. I have traveled with my work ever since," he says.

An exporting entrepreneur in his early 40s, Murali tells me that he lives in the southern region of India now, 400 kilometers from his native city. With his extensive travel schedule, I ask how often he gets to his home village.

"Every year," he says. His dark eyes are piercing and certain. "I travel home every year to worship at my temple. It is wonderful."

Murali tells me about the full day at his home temple, with 150 families together from sunrise to sunset. He even clears napkins from the bar and a tray of mixed nuts to diagram the generations and linkages of men who worship with him. He continues worship traditions in his new city, of course, but explains how each region of India will have varied approaches and styles.

"There are 24 states in India and more than 24 languages," he says. "Even 60 miles away, there is a different language. The celebrations are similar, but will look different from region to region."

"After living away for so long," I ask, "does your native city always feel familiar when you visit or oddly foreign?" Murali has been cordial with me so far, but understandably guarded. He lets his first smile peek through when I ask about "home."

"My native city is always home." Murali says. He pauses for a moment, his face becoming serious again, and adds, "Things do change; green fields are now homes or shops. Everywhere in the world, things are becoming commercialized. Still, we appreciate tradition."

I ask about these traditions and Murali lists just a few of the festival celebrations from his culture. There's a River Festival, a Sun Festival, a festival for studies and a festival for the harvest. Each month, he says, there is a different celebration with a different focus, and even a different food.

"Each celebration is regenerating," he says. "If you think about it, the total of these celebrations are essential for human beings," he says.

"Which is your favorite?" I ask.

"Diwali," he says, taking my journal and pen to write the title correctly. Diwali, Festival of Lights, is held in November or October and is India's biggest and most important holiday of the year. It is named for the rows of clay lamps that Indians light outside their homes, symbolizing the inner light that protects us from spiritual darkness.

"Every family will have new dress, there are firecrackers and sweets, servants get bonuses, brothers will visit sisters. It is a time for families to come together," he says. "The first Diwali after a couple is married is a big celebration for the entire family. The first Diwali with my own wife was in 2000. It will always be my favorite."

"As a kid, did you value these traditions," I ask, "or did you learn to really appreciate them once you were an adult?" Murali didn't hesitate: he's always cherished his culture and traditions.

"In my childhood, we woke up at 4:30 in the morning to be at the temple by 5am. We all were there, praying to God," he says. "We all prayed with the same movements. We had the same ritual of exercise. We all eat our evening meals on a new banana leaf. There is even a way to lay in the bed. Yes, these things create a culture, but they are also essential to the body."

I think about his world and the certainty it suggests. I can admit to wrinkling my Western nose at the notion of binding traditions, focused too intently on their restrictions. In talking with Murali and witnessing the joy he holds in simply describing his traditions to me, I'm better able to appreciate the sense of foundation and purpose that is acquired.

The more Murali tells me about his village, holidays, rituals and memories, the more relaxed and talkative he becomes. He speaks from a grounded place, a clear understanding of his journey through the world.

"Ancient priests wrote many things about timing. Every second, for example, three people are born in the world," Murali says, settling back against his chair, his eyes fixed on mine. "The destiny and the ancestry of those three people can be charted by the sun and the stars. The people born just one second later will have a different destiny. Our ways are ancient. This is what we believe."

As much as our cultures may differ, I learn that Murali and I share quirky similarities. First of all, we were born only eight days apart. Secondly, we are both raising preteen girls. Third, we both have surrendered our memory to digital gadgets.

"When I started my business, I kept 200 phone numbers in my head," he says. "Now with the mobile phone, there's no need." I laugh because the only number I have committed to memory is my mother's. (If I ever lose my digital address book and find myself in an epic crisis with only one permitted phone call, I'll have to cross my fingers that she's not in the audience of a stage play with her ringer silenced.)

"The young people now are a digital generation," Murali continues. "Anything they need to know, they pick up their phone and have an answer in seconds. We used to memorize everything."

I ask if he uses technology readily or reluctantly. "Oh, I use it," he says. "I have to. For business, conversations that used to take a week or two weeks happen instantly now."

I ask if he uses programs like Skype to talk with his daughter while he's on the road. Murali loosens his second broad smile. "Whatever it takes," he says. "Every Sunday when I am home, she asks questions about my travels. So many questions. I miss that."

I smile. Love and family are certainly universal concepts ... and food. Murali turns to greet a delivery person with a fragrant bag of takeout.

"Food from my country," he says to me with a smile.

I begin to pack my things, and thank him profusely for his time and generous cultural lesson. Murali pays for his dinner and settles his bag atop the bar. He turns his attention back to me and gives a slow nod.

"You are most welcome," he says. "Next time, I will tell you about Indian food. That will take an entire day."

TABLE WITH A VIEW

The server leaned into their table, close enough to transform their now-foursome into an intimate huddle. Her smile was broad and brilliant. The furthest edges, though, were unconvincing. The tiny corners where mustard, spittle and crumbs tend to gather without permission. Her corners were clean, but out of alliance with the rest of her smile. There, in the unremarkable intersection of flesh, he first saw her unsavory secret.

I call dibs on Happily Ever After.

FB STATUS :: APRIL 20 2010

Fellas, it's perfectly fine to say that you were just "aiiight" in sports. I mean, really, the statistical probability of allllll these blew-out-my-knee, got-caught-up, scouted-since-the-fifth-grade stories are just too much. High school was a long time ago. No one's judging you about the JV squad anymore. I promise.

FB STATUS :: JULY 15 2013

Not sure how I feel about God and Jesus having FB groups. If They start ignoring prayers --the way we ignore work-- to upload photos, update their statuses and post YouTube links ...this could all end very badly.

FB STATUS :: APRIL 16 2009

Definitely on a wild goose chase, but I anticipate a succulent and tasty lil bird

FB STATUS :: NOV 9 2009

I'm the kind of woman to make you wanna RE [-calibrate, -consider, -locate, -duce, -joice, -build, -appear, -vise, -generate, -mark, -think, -alize, -spect...] #you'vebeenwarnedBoo

FB STATUS :: Oct 22 2010

PURPOSE

The pot is indifferent to urgent heat
belching and rumbling beneath
its contents of soup, noodles,
oatmeal, frozen carrots

Sturdy and resistant, this red pot
settles against the fire
High or medium
Lid or no lid
It doesn't care
Just waits to be emptied,
washed and reasonably stacked
I wish, somehow, it could be more involved

TRUMP TIGHT

Black Queen rides silent
Tucked like ammunition
between paupers and kings
She falls back but never folds in

In the company of regal men,
hustlers, lovers, jokers and native sons
Black Queen be that secret
Sliding faces across tables
Paying attention to what's been tossed and kept

Black Kings play like revival, like
deep breaths, like mumbled codes,
like jazz riffs, like a hand shake, like
four and a possible
Everything is possible around this table

Black Jacks act a fool
about numbers stacking on their side
Us / Them
Win / Lose
Don't play out of turn
Get caught reneging on your word

Fifty-two chances
to play the world into your palm
Bid your hand
Cut the deck
Collect the kitty
Pack your bags for an eastbound train

SKY LESSONS
FROM ANITA BEE

You recall looking up to summer skies
A sheer filter of crystalline blue between you and heaven
It looked even bigger to you then
Impossible

A palette of green grass
Hugged your small body one blade at a time
You remember the patch of earth
cool against your back
tickling your neck
An easy comfort for resting your head, so full
of new thinking

You did not know how to lasso the clouds
with those fresh thoughts, still awkward
and unwieldy between your ears

You were afraid to name the clouds with
your soft, wet words
Clouds scrolled like silent movies across your blue sky
Your small lips pucker into a whisper:
    Elephant, you said
    Kitten, you said
    Cereal bowl
    Mama's good church shoe, you said
You learned to transcribe cumulous tales of summer
Trust your untethered translations

Then you pointed up your chin up to the darkness
Searching the firmament for comets, for
guideposts, for wishes, for shadowed
truth
You do not track the stars anymore
Do not measure fate by darkening rains

You rarely affix new names to the clouds
Rarely allow their molecules
to gather beneath your tongue

But the stories you scrawled across summer days will call
you back, one day
The sacred songs of midnight sorrows will lulluby your
soul, one day
You will see the florid script of your legacy clustered in
frosted breath
in smoke
in promises
in poems
in clumsy kisses
in prayers you sealed private for God

You will once again search this sky
for the forgotten names and prayers
you floated upward like a child's balloon
like a wish upon a star
like gospel on a cloudless day
Even if you never think of me, look up
Suspend the fear snaking
the length of your convictions
Look up, remember the bravery
you gnawed with abandon
Look up
Pin new names to a slow-rolling grace

When I laid beside you, beneath
the choreography of clouds, I called them:
    Frog
    Cupcake
    Roller skate
    God
I always knew that behind
this blue sky was God

From here, the sky is still so big
Impossible
A shimmering blue to stretch between you
and me, between homecoming and homegoing
Heaven and heaven bound

I always knew I was heaven bound
Summer sky words have ushered me home

God is impressive.

FB STATUS :: MAY 16 2013

MOAN

The notion
of your kiss
whispers along my spine
Anticipation scores my creases
Fold me
invitation easy

The caps of my knees
burnished in your ginger dew
Scrubbed pure for new
dirty smudges

My arms curl toward the ceiling
Slip from me like coiling smoke
I am vaporous
Hoping for the familiar
capture of your fingers
between your biceps, inside abandon
beneath a kiss

The promise
of your kiss
paints shadows across my shoulders
I bundle lithe and searching limbs
beneath the covers
and moan
close my eyes
close my eyes
and moan
close my eyes
close my eyes
and remember
kissing
you

INCANTATION NO. 2

Let me love you

Let me settle across your surfaces
gentle and insistent as dust
Elemental atoms gathered at your seams and corners
Lay myself humble against your natural grains
        Let me love you

I want to bend into your attention
A radio tune you didn't intend to learn
Urge your mouth around the lyrics of my name
again and again
I can be your classic for the ages
        Let me love you

Let me press my fingers into you
Keyboard confident
asdf jkl; without looking
I would ink your best intentions
across torn parchment
Read the epic tale of your heartbeat
until the gilded edge of slumber

Let me mist the slope of your brow
Speckle your flesh with salted dew
Course your sculpture of spine
temple, cheekbones, your neck
Feel me collecting in your basin and ravines

I have glittering gems embedded in these kisses
I would use them to adorn your crown

There's a vibration that hums behind my chest
Steady your navigation here
Let me love you with the urgent howl of birth

Grit my teeth, nurse your dreams
Forgive the agony of stretching
just to gaze at the wonder
blooming in your eyes

Let me unwind
these alloy springs
Convert anxious physics into faithful mechanics

Let the shoreline of these open arms
harbor the vastness of your seas

Maybe
      just maybe
      you should
          let me
               love you

LAUNDRY

He actually had a speech
Had the words scotch taped
across the back of his mind
He wanted to say it right

When that diamond beveled beam
flashed across her, when her eyes
were at that angle
Her mouth easy and sweet
He saw her for the first time
Wanted her for the first time
All over, again
He wanted to say it right

She's trying to do the laundry
He can deliver his speech
while she loads the clothes
But she tickles his ear with a smile
His arms pull her close
to his chest, to his lips

He feels her last twig of reason snap away
Not to / Not now
She kisses him from her insides
Loosens the leash on her hunger
Leans back against the dryer
His mass follows her curves
Shift weight to raise hips onto the Kenmore

He clips the back of her knees
in the hook of his hands
Only her legs are held back now
Her honor and dishonor are safe here
The smell of her moist and sweet soil
Luring his kisses closer

Like a tropical flower with some exotic name
she unfolds in majestic leisure
He loves to watch her bloom
Swallow her down to the stem

He etches this portrait of her pleasure
across the sum of his days
Marks each sunrise with evidence of her bliss
He wanted to tell her something like that
Assemble some patchwork of boy talk
to drape and quilt her sanctuary

He actually had a speech

He'll try again
to tell her, first,
next time

THE HONEST TRUTH

"You can't catch me! You can't catch me!" a preschooler sings in front of the house next door. I look out but can't see her. I remember the bouncy pitch of that age. Words still gooey in some spots.

"You can't catch me..."

I walk away from the screen door and pick up the dust rag I'd left on the floor. I oil and wipe, oil and wipe, mindful —as my mother warned— to "clean under and not around" the frames and figurines. She had to remind me of that often as a kid. After a while, she took to emphasizing "around" by stretching the vowels all the way out. "Arouuuuuuuuuund," like this was the part of the directions I wasn't getting. Well, I learned that having to re-do chores, in a word, sucked. So I stopped making my mother stretch her words out of shape. Now, I still clean *under* the knick knacks.

Truth be told, cleaning is simply more satisfying when it's done well. I usually only find time to "tidy" these days. So, cleaning like this tends to happen in sporadic, Olympic bursts. Out of the blue, I might power wash the shower walls. Take a toothbrush to faucet fixtures. Drag out the carpet shampoo. It could happen. It could.

Today, dusting happened. Probably because my spirit needed it more than the book shelves. If there's a zen to cleaning house, I can get there: music, rote and methodical mechanics, plenty of wide open mental space for my thoughts to stretch and move around.

The new family of thoughts moved in today. Awkward. Tentative. Even though I expected them. I didn't know which post-divorce emotions would come around, so I've been braced for the worst. I mostly anticipated pangs of guilt. Certainly, I wrestled with my decision and how it would forever affect the people I cared about, including my ex-husband. At the end of the day, radioactivity guilt is not the emotion that seems to be settling in.

Instead, it's an unnerving sense of vulnerability. In between the emotional grooves of "how," "why," and "what next," I feel both infallible and morbidly flawed.

This weekend, I spent the day in Chicago visiting old friends, Crystal and Randy. Crystal and I worked together at a swanky bar when I lived there. I was a cocktail waitress; she was a bartender; and Randy was one of the regulars who eventually became her biggest fan. They reconnected some years later, flirted, dated, married, struggled, renewed, prospered, reproduced, rejoiced and, now they take drives through tony Chicago neighborhoods to imagine which houses could one day be theirs.

These are the random marital reminders I don't yet know what to do with. Sadness might be a default assumption, but sad is not quite how I feel. Instead I'll think, "I don't have this anymore." No slow violins, no mournful glance skyward or heavy lids, no clenched fists. I just don't have it anymore. A co-dreamer. Bracelet-fastener. Hand-holder. Attitude-checker. Getter-of-my-jokes. I don't have it. This is called "coming to terms," I suppose.

Still, I'm staying alert, monitoring myself objectionably close these days. I don't *think* I would become bitter, lonely, distant or depressed, but what would I know about the aftermath of ending an 11-year marriage? Nothing. What I **do** know is that my decision was unquestionably the right one. I do know that I'm cushioned in a new sense of peace and that I'm optimistic about the future.

But there are days when I don't feel so solid in this new footing. When I'm not sure whether I'm sure. Those days, like today, are great for cleaning, especially when the promise of summer is gliding on the breeze through my new screen door and precious little girls are singing from the sidewalk.

Oil and wipe. Oil and wipe. I'll be one hundred percent again soon.

Oil and wipe. You can't catch me. You can't catch me.

STOP AHEAD

He watched Margie's breast plate rise and fall while she spoke. Inflate. Deflate. The large square freckles assigned faithfully across her skin. He wanted to rest his head there again, his hair damp from a shower and his slim shoulders bundled in the blue towels she'd bought for them. His father's other girlfriends had not known about the stores where bath towels were softest, sweet cereal came in dual packs, and night lights had faces like Saturday cartoons.

Carmen had been the first girlfriend after mom left. She had brought them clogged drains. Angel seldom wore long pants. Kim hadn't last two holidays. Paula had only existed in Sunday morning giggles from behind a closed bedroom door.

Aunt Paige had called them all "chicks," telling her twin —his father—that they were too "young and dumb" for his time. His father only said that women had sign posts pitched awkwardly in their conversations: Yield. Dip. Bridge out. Stop. He was relearning how to read their warnings.

Aunt Paige never called Margie a chick. His father never called her at all. She always arrived by halftime. With a carton of milk. Bottle of rum. She always appeared with a smile. Usually left before it could fade.

Her voice was diaphanous as curtain sheers bouncing behind a breeze, but her chest seemed powerful to him. Inhale. Exhale. He watched while she read her magazines. Inhale and exhale. While she folded the towels. Inhale. While she waited for that last taxi cab. Exhale. When she turned to him with a sad wave.

His father kept bringing home girlfriends with their road sign warnings, but neither of them stopped wishing for lost freckles, plush bath towels and open roads.

Pulled on a pair of slacks that said, "...what was that, about not working out today?"

FB STATUS :: DEC 18 2012

Lay it down. That burden, right there? The one that you never deserved? The one you lifted to your shoulders long ago as a punishment? Or, maybe, that one over there... the one that doesn't even belong to you? Yes. It's time. Lighten your soul's load and lay that burden down.

FB STATUS :: DEC 12 2012

3rd Grader: Are you building up our esteem?
Me: I hope so.
3rd Grader: So, you tell us our papers are good when they're not so we can feel good about ourselves? *wow face* Me: Uhhh....that won't help your papers get better, huh...?
He gives me a little grin and goes back to work. These little humans are sharp; don't get it confused, grown ups. I thought about saying "your picture is ugly but I'm proud of your effort" but, apparently, he knew that's what I meant all along ... lol

FB STATUS :: FEB 1 2013

Giggling at the innate liberties of Older SiblingNess: Child #1 has convinced Child #2 that Rocks, Paper, Scissors now includes "Volcano," "Tweezers" & "Knife."

FB STATUS :: JAN 4 2009

CARD ACADEMY

My mind is superimposing a 30-year-old snapshot over this present-day scene. My father is on the carpet, propped on his side with one arm. My sister, two daughters and I sit in a semi circle around him, a deck of playing cards shuffled and divided among us.

I remember this.

He's explaining the game of Dirty Hearts like he was a reading an excerpt from *The Iliad*. My father is hardly a florid or theatrical man, but he can make explanations feel monumental or deconstruct an abstraction —like love or racism— into black-and -white grids of logic.

After his career as a military officer, I hoped Daddy might become an educator. I could imagine him as the unyielding middle school teacher pushing unsuspecting underachievers to unexpected personal heights. Or as the unflappable college professor with "sold out" course sections every semester. Sadly, he wasn't the least bit interested in classrooms or lecture halls (he also has an exhausted tolerance for insolence and bureaucracy). Luckily for my sister, my daughters and me, classes at the Card Academy are in full swing.

The girls are 11 and 12 years old. My sister and I were around the same ages when we learned to play Dirty Hearts, Gin Rummy and Spades. We spent a lot of time playing board games and cards then, as that was also our phase for spending a lot of time being alternately grounded. On those week-long stints of no TV, radio, outside or friends, the "free" sister would honor an unspoken truce of sibling solidarity and keep the other one company for a spell. Even when we weren't being confined, we played.

Daddy's tutorial with the girls transitions from  Setup to Operations to Rules to Strategy, quizzing them along the way. My sister and I trade knowing grins as the girls listen to my father in earnest. He made us all feel like we were starting an archaeological dig, about to disassemble a hydrogen bomb or draft the verbiage for a new nation's constitution. Much to consider, but definitely manageable, as long as you remember how to pass along the Queen of Spades ...

Our practice rounds go horribly at first, and the girls slowly get the hang of the game. Each direction imparts so much of himself: intelligence, humor, wisdom, patience and discipline. Even if they don't become lifelong players, I am grateful that they've had this early moment with my father. They can never know their "Poppy" the  same way my sister and I know him as "Daddy." He's sharing instructions for a card game but it sounds like a love song to me.

IVORY BANGLE LADY

Dig my hole deep
Intern legacy with my bones
Coat my rich skin
with thick oils
olive, rosehip, pomegranate, shea
Even in death
Even in death

Dig my hole deep
Retire brilliant baubles
along the contours of my waist
beads, cologne, blue glass, ivory
Send me with greetings for God
Send me with greetings for God

Dig my hole deep
Entomb the artifacts and gleam
of my inimitable and glorious people
wealth, intellect, melanin and truth
History will not bury me
History will not bury me

The Ivory Bangle Lady
"This skull is particularly interesting, because the stone
sarcophagus she was buried in, and the richness of the
grave goods, means she was a very wealthy woman,
absolutely from the top end of York society. Her case
contradicts assumptions that immigrants are low status
and male, and that African individuals are likely to have
been slaves." ~Dr. Hella Eckhard, Archeology
Dept., University of Reading (UK)

FORGETTING

We still speak of blood
inside our silence
Wordlessly drum fingers across raw walls of flesh
We do not rush past
We do not smear waste on our slacks
We do not swill and spit red bombs
on the ground

We still speak of blood
with mouths clamped quiet around indignation
settled solidly beneath our tongues
Withering and barnacled,
ancient arguments fall apart in
thick sediment

We still communicate a bloody anguish
when we are not speaking of new days
When we are not practicing fluent forbearance
This fresh language
airing out the stagnant smells

We are facing forward
Deciphering new stories inside the winds
Heavy memories anchor our backs
We speak of them
bloody
in silence

"Just because I don't demand much, doesn't mean
you shouldn't give everything."

FB STATUS :: OCT 30 2010

RUSTED KNOT

Rust can be defined as the destructive attack
of metal --through interaction with the surround-
ing environment-- when the oxygen in water dis-
solves against iron.

Amid the patterning of steel links
We are inevitable
Settled along the perimeter
        near the center
    everywhere you choose not to look

We are here
Clinging sharp edges to an ideal
We are the rusted knot of wire
Glaring and belligerent
Evidence of the flawed existence we all share
Post to post, we define the science of society
Dividing haves by the square root of have nevers

Our twist of metal intersecting
standards of the greater fence
A blight against the glimmer
A weakening of our prescription
        from "protection" to "barrier"
We concentrate in layers and generations
America's process of rot

We snarl eyesores into the landscape
of your bar graphs
your news print
your short drive home
that little bar with the amazing sangrias
We trumpet your arrival in
the hinges of Auntie's screen door
We are not concerned with

refracting glints of sunlight
We resist the slathering and sprays
aimed at halting our oxidation
Corrosion is a byproduct of
integrating raw elements

Our fate flakes away
in slow suffering

INCANTATION NO. 3

A streetlight hangs above my window
spilling diffused light onto my bed
I've claimed its luminescence as
my very own moon
Prying apart the darkness
as we peel back the sheets
Fling wide this zodiac
Fly against the night
False moonlight swirling across naked skin

I delight in five-point kisses
dotting stars along my sides and thighs and
navel and knees
Tie me down in moonbeams
Tease me with quasar smoke until I orbit
until I float
until my back arches a new constellation

Hold me close
Caress the dark matter embedded in my flesh
Eclipsing earthbound lovers, we soar
the parallels. Swallow black holes. Slide butt naked
across Saturn's rings
Glow magnificent in this
lunar bliss

You are welcome
to board my spacecraft again real soon
Only an inter-galactic life form can please a woman
with her very own moon

You might not believe this all the way deep down on the inside, but I want to confirm that YOU are bigger and stronger than the things you're afraid of. F'real. So, how about you go ahead and shine today...

FB STATUS :: JULY 26 2010

I'm scoffing at this Back to School supply list. A protractor? Teachers are still making kids bring protractors? I never, ever used mine. The compass thing-y either. Oh, wait... I wonder if that would explain some of my grades in math..

FB STATUS :: AUG 27 2012

I heard "will power" is overrated. Of course, it was a turtle sundae that said it...who heard it from a slice of carrot cake... Sketchy resources, at best

FB STATUS :: SEPT 19 2012

Every word we speak falls onto someone's soil. Are you scattering seeds for vibrant greenery or raggedy weeds?

FB STATUS :: July 10 2009

CONFESSIONS OF A HUGGER

For a thousand different reasons, I've been long re-moved from the schmooze circuit of banquets, happy hours and receptions. I attended an awards reception for a local women's organization recently and found myself relieved that I'd changed my mind about bailing at the last minute. I reconnected with colleagues, introduced myself to future program partners and hugged a long-lost mentor or two.

I'm back! I thought to myself.

One of the faces I hadn't seen in a few years belonged to a woman who runs a mentoring program for up-and-coming community organizers. I can't say I know her particularly well. Like, we hadn't "done lunch" or coffee together, but we had earnest ambitions of working together once. I was feeling socially euphoric and it was good, even, to see her.

Our paths crossed, literally, as I was leaving the wine bar and she was moving toward the foyer. We approached one another and I stepped in to greet her with a hug.

Big mistake.

As I cupped the back of her arms and leaned in to lightly brush our cheeks (the standard Social Hug for Professionals), I realized I was actually pulling her toward me. Her shoulders stiffened like planks and, through her shock, she returned a reluctant one-two back pat (the standard Stop Touching Me Hug for All Occasions).

With permission, I'm definitely the touchy-feely hugger-of-strangers type, but I'm not the brand of warm-and-fuzzy who assaults unwitting victims with my over-flow of affection.

"I'm a hugger," I typically warn, keeping my distance with one outstretched arm so that the potential hug partner has the option to accept my personal contact or to just shake my hand.

This time, unfortunately, I hadn't afforded the handshake option and had already broken her barrier of personal space. As I pulled away, I felt her chest release a tiny, captured gasp of breath and noted the melting panic in her eyes. Only the outline of a frozen smile remained. I felt pretty badly.

Check that: I didn't just feel badly. I felt a bit creepy. Slinking back to my table, I wondered if I'd been mistaken in thinking she liked me in the first place. Had I done or said something to offend her or her organization over the past two years? Was I emitting an end-of-day funk? Did she find public displays and the people who commit them inappropriate? Was she a hardcore feminist stereotype who abhorred "soft" business women? Was she a wounded individual with profound intimacy issues?

Or maybe…

Just maybe…

She didn't like to hug people.

I'll be honest: the last consideration didn't occur to me for a few days. In an unrelated conversation with a close friend from college, part of the story she was telling me included the statement, "…and I don't do hugs too much, anyway …"

So—that's a real thing?

And here I'd wasted brain juice analyzing my colleague's presumed brokenness.

I imagine it's these ego-centric metrics that guide charismatic supervisors to mistakenly measure their team members in decibels rather than decision-making; for suburban-bred teachers to assess students' stability based on picket fences or neatly-packed lunches rather than on persistence and even temperaments; for lovers to

---

Love it when the voices in my head are getting along.

FB STATUS :: JAN 25 2011

calculate longevity through compliments paid rather than commitments kept.

True, we're inclined to see the world only with the eyes we've been given, but there are other panoramas to embrace and I appreciate being reminded of that.

Otherwise, there might be a poster hanging in your local post office about a Serial Hugger skulking through a neighborhood near you.

Considering how grocery shopping when you're
hungry can be costly, I wonder if the same
logic holds true about going to a nightclub
with a grumbling libido.

FB STATUS :: FEB 27 2009

Eating chicken wings, talking on the phone with my
doctor about high cholesterol.
"...mmporh mmgor grrlthm mmmhmm..."

FB STATUS :: NOV 17 2009

Selling snacks at a youth event. Everything's a dollar.
My 11-year-old is (wo)manning the shop.
One of the kids only had 95 cents.
He did NOT get any snacks. Lol

FB STATUS :: DEC 14 2012

Hey. Hey. HEY!!! *smooths front of dress, restores
cool* Hey ... just wanted to remind you that some
of these days are supposed to be hard.
Supposed to. It's right here in The Contract.
*adjusts your collar, cups your shoulders, offers
a sympathetic smile* So, how about putting
the tantrum on pause and knocking out
the rest of this week, hmmm?

FB STATUS :: NOV 26 2013

SMOKE

Peri lay beneath the pewter sky and waited for heaven to explode.

The grass, spiked hard with frost, raked the backs of her shoulders and thighs. She tried lifting herself from the ground, rising as high as her fingertips and toes before folding back into the ground. The winter air gnawed at her skin. Sirens wailed toward the house.

Her thoughts were mottled with rum, but the pain screaming up the length of her leg confirmed she was not trapped inside a dream. She was not nodding on the train. She was not daydreaming while her hands maneuvered bath towels into trifolds. She was not spooning on the second floor. She was, in fact, crumpled on the cold ground, wearing nothing but a t-shirt, trying to wish away the worst of her decisions.

Red lasers whipped at the smoky darkness. A riot of horns, engines and boots stormed the property in urgent choreography. Peri closed her eyes. Voices zoomed near and voices galloped past her into the house. The mounting clamor felt distant, but her leg reminded her that she was wide awake.

Fingers pressed against her wrist. Hands lifted her from the grass onto a gurney. Covered her mouth with an oxygen cup. Tightened a blood pressure cuff around her bicep. Draped a blanket over her bare arms and thighs. She felt herself nodding as the questions floated toward her: Could she hear them? Was she hurt? Had she been alone in the house?

The firefighter tending to her rested a hand on her shoulder while he pressed a stethoscope to her chest. Her hair was a thick avalanche of spirals and fuzz and he was careful to brush aside her tangled mane to find her shoulder. His hand was commanding and comforting. Peri had thought the same of Carter's hands only hours ago. Kneading her shoulders, tracing the rounded curve of her hip, bridling the mounting swivel in her waist.

The firefighter elevated her mangled leg, brokering instructions through her nods and stunned silence. Other voices bantered flatly inside hand-held radios. Jets of water raced from hoses. She heard heavy feet stomping across the porch and the freshly polished floors inside. The house groaned as it surrendered timber, glass and air. Acid tears burned the corners of Peri's eyes. This house had saved her once.

She tried to push words from her throat, filling her chest with thick sobs. The firefighter coaxed her to keep the mask on, to keep breathing. She coughed and cringed as he addressed her leg, snarled by glass and splintered wood from her leap out of the bathroom window. A crunch of footsteps approached them.

"Miss, can you hear me?" the footsteps said.

Peri nodded her head, training her gaze on gleaming black shoes.

"My name is Lieutenant Fordham," he said. "Are you able to answer a few questions?"

Peri nodded again.

"What is your name?"

"Peregrine Matthews," she said, wincing. Her voice, normally high and girlish, was raspy and worn. The firefighter, still by her side, gave her shoulder a little squeeze.

"How do you know Maura McDermott?" Lieutenant Fordham asked.

Peri raised her eyes from his feet to his face. He was an angular man, with taught, sharp features, a prim mouth and searching green eyes. He reminded her of a cartoon, an animated grasshopper.

"Friend," Peri croaked. "Client."

"Where is Ms. McDermott?" he asked.

"Vacation," Peri said.

"Does she know you're here?"

Peri shook her head, shame snaking up her side. Behind the lieutenant, Peri spied the blackening building that had been her friend's inheritance and livelihood and a sanctuary for Peri when her own apartment —or skull— felt too small.

"You were alone?" he asked.

In that moment, she imagined the spectacle of a half-dressed black woman sprawled on the lawn of a high-end bed and breakfast farmhouse. She was long accustomed to raised eyebrows in these exclusive environs, but a ravenous fire at a property she neither owned nor resided at trumped any thoughts of indignation.

Peri had first worked at the inn back in high school, when Maura only rented the house for special events. They had giggled themselves into tears, one discovering the other hiding in a guestroom away from the glossed and gibbering guests downstairs and out on the lawn. Peri's mother had carried the grace and charm for them all. Entertaining and socializing had been her art, especially among this ilk. She had been a gleaming onyx gem amid hard clusters of opal and pearl.

Maura said Peri's mother had always been an irrefutable exception to irreducible social rules. They'd been paired as roommates in college and had gone from sharing a dorm to sharing a loft apartment, interview shoes, cruise photos and, eventually, a matching set of divorces. When Peri's parents finally met, Maura insisted that her father never had a chance, though he'd tried to fight the absurdity of a blue chip executive with a black wife. But Peri's mother was beguiling and irresistible to anyone who met her. Maura had witnessed their elegant social bloodshed, babysat for their two preschoolers destined for ebony-and-ivory step-dom, had worn a celery-colored gown in their wedding, and kissed Peri's bald almond-colored head on the day she was born.

When the plane crash snapped Peri's mother into two distinct pieces, gone from their family was her sly grin, her artful eye, and her curated words. Gone was their polymer. Maura had lost her own mother, as well as her uterus, earlier that year but tried to lay her crude edges and clunky conversation across the void in her friend's family. Peri had been in middle school, her sister a junior in high school and her brother in his first year of college. Her father's boutique public relations agency was scrapping for larger accounts in those days. None of them had been proficient at navigating the loss, but Peri had seemed intent on self-destructing first.

Peri had measured her teens and most of her twenties in grams, tequila shots, condoms and potential last breaths. Her sister and father had drifted from reach by the time she turned 30, but her brother and Maura remained vital touchstones. In fact, they'd pleaded for Peri to help with the inn once it became a bed and breakfast and she had raged back at them, against their privilege, against her shame.

Cleaning brought Peri closest to peace. She still lived at a gallop, but spinning herself into cocoons of quiet and polish gave her a center of gravity and a promise that, finally, would not snarl back at her. Now, against the hazy and emerging dawn, the inn was blackening beyond the lieutenant's shoulder. Peri squeezed her eyes tight.

"Miss Matthews?" Fordham prompted. "Were you in the house alone?"

"Yes," she said. "Yes."

The firefighter, who'd been busying himself with her leg bandages interjected, "She's ready for transport when you're done." To Peri he said, "We're going to St. Phillip's to take care of that leg. Stitches for sure, but surgery might be necessary too. Other than that, I think you're going to make it."

He gave Peri a wink and she managed a weak grin in return. Lieutenant Fordham advised her to expect his visit. A knot hardened in the center of her gut, like that summer she and her sister were bicycling home from the park and their dog got hit by a car. Peri had been told not to take the beagle with them and had felt this same clot of guilt, loss and heartbreak. She had stayed with the dog, the hard cement biting into her knees until her sister and father returned with their mother's lap to bawl into.

Peri wept silently this time. The firemen folded her gurney into an ambulance and sealed her inside. Through the small windows, she saw currents of smoke obscuring the sky. She thought about Carter, imagined his taxi cab departure. In concert, their tongues whipped brilliant repartees. In discord, they sprayed wicked venom. Her last quip —something about the weak currency of his word— had made him curse her viciously as he stomped into his boxers and down the stairs.

"Have you seen them?"

Peri blinked herself back from the four-poster bed, back from cabinets and doors slamming on the first floor, back to the gurney, the ambulance ride and the smooth-faced firefighter. Still, she was confused.

"Fishbone," he said, nodding to her t-shirt.

Peri looked down at the skeletal fish logo. She'd plucked the shirt from Carter's pile on the floor, wanting to drape herself while he rained out his tantrum down-stairs. Returning to find her covered would serve as a shorthand reprimand, though she intended for him peel her naked all over again.

"No," Peri said to the fireman, thinking of Carter's regular raves about the ska band. "Not yet."

"I keep hearing they put on one helluva show," he said, "but I haven't met anyone who's actually been."

Peri nodded, then started to cough.

"Take it easy," he said. "Almost there."

The fireman's eyes lingered on her for an extra heartbeat and Peri's jaw tightened. She had long hair, but it was wild. Her hips were narrow, but her ass was round. Her skin was brown, but it did not blend with evening dusk. She carried the King's English in her mouth and rancid anger on the tip of her tongue. When she was small, strangers regularly had tapped her mother's shoulder to remark on how adorable she was. Peri's "precious" had matured easily into "pretty," despite her sister's warning about mixed kids losing their cuteness as they got older.

"Black don't crack," her sister would say. Cocoa-colored and regally beautiful, her sister had taunted Peri with this, her only ammunition, rolling eyes at Peri's dangling curls or summer sunscreen.

Her brother, in contrast, was the spitting image of their father —brown hair, brown eyes, white skin—and carried only worthy words for Peri. He was mercifully unfazed that she was the only Matthews child wholly claimed by both parents. Peri was supposed to represent the best of them all but existed, instead, as a mulatto reminder of the toxicity of skin, family and silence.

"I think it's cool that you can date whomever you want these days," Peri's brother had said to her one summer. He was home from college and she was on her way to a pool party with her friends, most of whom were white back then. Black classmates had only offered her a rotation of hostility, fickleness, or indifference. Her sister had prepared her for something, at least.

"Be careful," her brother had said as the carload of blondes and redheads pulled into the drive. "I know guys at the frat house who hook up with black girls or Asian girls just to say they've done it. Don't be a stamp on some white guy's passport."

Peri had left the house in an annoyed huff, but her brother's warning had burrowed deep beneath that pool party, senior year bonfires and keggers during her single year of college. Peri had stopped trying to discern curiosity from attraction, friendships from fashion. She recycled disappointments and resentment instead.

The firefighter stiffened behind Peri's gaze and looked away, pinning his blue eyes to a clipboard. Peri let out a slow breath. She was exhausted from lugging ready-made confrontations. The hospital's emergency room signs were approaching, and she was tired.

"I know somebody," she said after he locked the gurney legs beneath her. "One helluva show."

The fireman looked down at her and nodded, a smile in his blue eyes.

Peri shielded her eyes from the florescent shock. The gurney wheels hummed across the tiles. She croaked answers to the intake nurse's questions about allergies and insurance and a cell number for her brother.

The fireman's blue eyes were soon replaced by brown eyes of a resident who sank one long needle into her calf and threaded another needle through her splayed flesh. Peri watched his swift hands pull, tug and knot at the open gash once, twice, until the room went black.

"Not that one."

Peri held the hanger beneath her chin and looked for the voice.

"The blue one," said the voice emerging from behind the mirrored column. She didn't recognize the lean, brown skinned man. He was not as much handsome as he was well-manicured in a smart bowtie, dark denim jeans, and funky, black frame glasses.

He stood at a respectful distance with his dark eyes fixed on her. She curdled her lip and returned to her image in the mirror.

"Is there a reason I should give a shit what you think?"

"Other than my being right? Maybe not," he said. "Maybe so."

Peri scaled him with a look. His princely stance did not waiver. With a suck of her teeth she dismissed him, tossing the blue dress and its hanger at his feet.

"Fuck outta here," she snarled, turning to face the dress rack.

"I told your brother you wouldn't remember me," he said, "but he's double parked and you weren't answering your phone."

Peri pivoted slowly to face him.

"He thinks we shared a moment at the cigar bar last night," the thin brown man continued. "He has no idea you were tweaked out of your mind. You probably had no idea where you were."

Peri stared at him, dumbfounded. He grinned wryly.

"Popped a little oxy after dinner, I'm guessing. Looked like the high was still wet," he said, sliding his hands into the front pockets of his jeans. "He's a good dude, your brother, but he's extra white sometimes, ain't he?"

Peri moved one hand to her hip.

"I fell in love with him anyway," the brown man said, pre-empting her tirade. Her mounting vitriol drained as Peri realized her mouth was hanging open. This was the "Regional Conference Dude" her brother had been cooing about for so many months. She couldn't believe she'd gotten so high. Or that this stranger was reading her like he knew her. Like he was somebody special. Like he was right.

"It means a lot to him that we get along this weekend, so that's what's going to happen, alright, Peregrine?" The brown skin man balanced a smile on his lips and knife points in his eyes. "I'm not even going to worry him with this oxy thing. Not now. Is that cool, Peregrine? Can we all just get along?"

The brown skinned man bent to pick up the blue dress from the floor and asked, "Are we taking this to the register, or no?"

Peri slowly returned to herself, burning his smirk with a steely glare. She reached out and grabbed the hanger, smashing the blue dress back to the ground.

He chuckled as she stormed past him. "I'm Brian," he called after her, "but everyone calls me Carter."

Carter secured a corporate transfer and relocated the following year. The three of them lived together and Peri served him the same chilly disregard as she had for her brother's previous boyfriends. Her brother laughed it off as standard procedure, but she and Carter knew differently. She was clean by then, but rejected Carter's conversation and concern.

"Why are you in my business all the fucking time?" she asked one day. They were setting up for a football party while her brother went to the store for barbecue sauce and napkins.

"You need somebody in your business," Carter said.

"What makes you think you know what I need?"

"Been here before, girlie," he said, dumping ice into a tin tub. "Nobody stays in your business, nobody knows when you're strung out again."

"I wasn't—"

"Semantics," Carter said firmly.

Peri groaned. "I can't wait to move out of here," she said.

"Yeah, well..." Carter said, nudging the ice tub into position.

Peri tossed a broccoli floret at his face. He batted it away and grinned triumphantly. Peri rolled her eyes.

"You're going to miss my ass," Peri said, then added, "not that you know anything about a woman's ass."

Peri looked up when silence filled the room instead of a snappy response. She was accustomed to tossing jokes at her brother, but she never meant to offend. Not even Carter.

The silence thickened, enveloping them, when Peri discovered Carter staring at her. His eyes crept over her slowly, intent like fire, and she knew.

Peri opened her eyes and felt the metal bed railing hard and cool against her forehead. She blinked a few times to confirm, again, that this was real. Leg pain. Stomach knot. House fire. Hospital bed. She looked around the room. Tracks of long curtains divided the beds and their patients, all wrapped in varying designs of bandages and gauze.

Peri tried to sit up, but the pinch of pain in her leg made her whimper. She patted the top of her blanket until she met the call paddle and pressed for the nurse's station. She heard the squish of tennis shoes a few minutes later, then ball bearings slid open the tall curtain.

"Right on time," the nurse said. "Had this ready. Figured you'd need it."

Peri grunted as the nurse hung a fresh drip bag and waddled around the bed to tug at the sheet and blanket, scoop empty water cups, andlay down a fresh bucket of ice chips.

"Aim for this if you feel sick," the nurse said, sliding a plastic yellow pan on the table beside her. "The morphine makes some people sick when they wake up. There's a man here for you. Not your brother, though. He should be here soon. He'll have light brown hair, you say? I think that's great. My grandson dated a black girl once. Nice girl."

Peri gave the nurse a weary look. The nurse continued, impervious.

"Anyhoo, this guy is a fire marshal or something," she said. Peri's shoulders drooped. She was hoping the visitor might be Carter. "He's been waiting awhile. Doctor says I gotta send him back. Wipe your mouth, sweetie."

As the nurse's tennis shoes retreated, Peri closed her mouth around the straw and drank. Hard soles crossing the room and stopped at her open curtain. She replaced the cup of water and took a deep breath. The morphine drip was working.

"How are you holding up, Miss Matthews?" Lieutenant Fordham asked.

I'm gonna hafta punch this week in the face...

FB STATUS :: NOV 14 2011

"Holding," Peri said, managing to push herself upright in the bed.

"I'm sorry to disturb your rest," he said, "but it's always best for us to connect the dots sooner than later."

"Dots?"

Lieutenant Fordham stood to one side at the end of the bed. "This is going to sound like a line from a really bad movie," he said, "but can you think of anyone who might want to harm you or your boyfriend?"

Peri gawked at the Lieutenant. Harm her? Boyfriend?

"I- I don't have-- what do you—what are you talking about?" she stammered.

The lieutenant rested his fingers on the top rail of the bed guard and said, "We learned two important facts at the burn site. The first thing is this fire was set deliberately."

Peri shook her head in stunned disbelief. The morphine was working too well.

"Had the inn been freshly painted?" he asked.

Maura had, in fact, planned to paint the inn that week. It was how she had timed her vacation. It was why Peri knew she and Carter would have the house to themselves. They had even joked about getting high on the paint fumes, but they'd laughed when they discovered Maura had only gotten as far as setting out cans of paint and turpentine all over the house and draping the furniture in drop cloths.

She nodded.

"We found cans of paint and turpentine in the basement, too," the lieutenant said.

She pictured Maura, with her sinewy tan arms, lifting the five gallon pails out of her SUV hatch, into the house, and up and down the stairs. Maura had undertaken countless projects at the inn that defied her small frame. Planting shrubs. Replacing a dishwasher. Erecting a carport for guests. Peri had often teased that Maura had the strength and determination of an ant.

"It seems a fan had blown stacks of newspapers into the furnace, igniting the cans downstairs and, of course, all of the cans upstairs once the fire started to climb."

"Sounds like an accident to me," Peri said, sorrow pulling again at her heart.

Lieutenant Fordham nodded at Peri. He wasn't agreeing with her, just responding to her. He was thoughtful for a moment. Peri worried about Maura.

"Have you talked to her yet?" she asked. "Does she know?"

"Can't get in touch with her," he said. "The only numbers on the property records are the number to the inn and a number for her brother. We called him but he wasn't exactly helpful."

Peri sighed. "Helpful is not his thing."

"Let me guess, he thinks the parents should've left the house to him?"

"Something like that," Peri said. She was uncomfortable unrolling Maura's family laundry. She'd never met Maura's brother, only lent an ear when Maura sputtered expletives at his frequent attempts to "fleece" her, as she put it, usually ending in a tearful rant about how his wretched life was his wretched fault.

"Something like that," Lieutenant Fordham repeated. "It seems he's been waiting on a check. Did you know he won a court judgment ordering Ms. McDermott to either surrender or sell the house?"

Peri raised her eyebrows in disbelief. On more than one occasion Maura had sadly explained how, even in death, she had to protect their parents from her brother's avarice and wickedness.

"Maura loves that place," Peri said. "Grew up in that house."

The lieutenant nodded, his eyes pointed down to his long fingers coiled around the bed rail. "Hate and love can force the best people to make the worst decisions," he said, "like removing all the batteries in the smoke detectors."

Peri felt uncomfortable under the lieutenant's gaze, but forced herself to stay calm.

Lieutenant Fordham mindlessly tapped the bed rail as he continued. "That fan I mentioned? It was plugged into a timer, like the kind you use to make your lamps turn on and off when you're not home. Peculiar, right?"

Peri's hand wanted to fly toward her mouth, but she gripped the bedspread instead. She hoped her brother would show up soon. She wanted to go home. She wanted to warn Maura. She wanted to see Carter.

"The other thing?" Lieutenant Fordham began, lilting his tone to make sure Peri was still following along. Peri looked up at him, foreboding creeping up from her toes. "We also learned that you had company last night."

Peri forced her eyebrows to furrow and pushed herself up higher in the bed. As a career liar, she knew not to speed into indignation. Confusion was the first step. Then victimization and injury. Then ramp up into belligerent outrage. It was her word against a smoldering house. She'd lied her way out of more impossible situations.

"I don't know what you mean," Peri said, looking at the lieutenant in earnest.

He nodded again and started talking about fire patterns and consumption time and smoke capacity and an extra cell phone and a second pair of shoes. One compartment of her brain prepared an explanation. The phones were hers, personal and business. The second pair of shoes was from the lost and found, and she'd slipped them on to take her smelly Thai takeout to the trash in the unexpectedly cold night air.

Lieutenant Fordham continued, describing the utter destruction of the kitchen and main floor. Peri relaxed even more. Explaining two jackets draped over the couch could have been one coincidence too many. Tough, but not impossible. Peri wore smug satisfaction behind her poker face as the lieutenant spoke.

"Gutted," he repeated. He folded his arms across himself, as if to pin his fidgeting fingers into obedience.

"No way we could've known that was a body in the downstairs bathroom."

Peri felt the air pulled out of her. She stared at Lieutenant Fordham, frozen and speechless.

"We would've left him there if he we hadn't found the shoes," Fordham continued.

After one long heartbeat, then another, Peri forced noisy breath from her lungs. She did not move, only tracked the lieutenant with her eyes. He nodded and looked down. His fingers danced along the railing again.

"Unless your *friend* is involved in some kind of criminal activity that routinely involves payback or homicide, our early guess is that this is a case of arson and you two picked the wrong weekend to … uh … catch up."

The lieutenant became a blur as Peri's eyes spilled with tears. Lieutenant Fordham walked around the bed to pull two tissues from the box waiting on a side table. He handed them to Peri.

"Not a criminal, right?" he asked, flatly.

Peri slowly shook her head.

"Alright, Miss Matthews," he said. "That's enough for now. I'm sorry about your night. Unfortunately, we'll have to be in touch again. I'm leaving my card on top of your property bag here."

Peri heard the hard taps of the lieutenant's receding footsteps, then a sudden quiet. The hum of monitors and murmur of conversations were distant from her, as if trapped between glass plates. Or maybe she was trapped. Maybe she had been pressed onto a slide and flattened for some stranger's evaluation. Species: Vile Human.

Peri counted all of the times she could've pulled away from Carter. After the first time, when Carter had knocked on her apartment door to deliver the purse she'd left behind on purpose. She'd kissed him and his tongue had been bitter like a drug. Several months later, the second time, he'd pulled her down beside the Christmas tree, where they climaxed while her brother napped. The next morning, Peri had sipped her coffee as Carter thanked her brother with a kiss, his Fishbone shirt and concert tickets staring up between them.

For three years, they'd carried on between weekend errands, inside appointment blocks held for meetings and luncheons and behind fake overnight business trips, like this one. This time, they'd agreed, was going to be their last, last time. Typical, they would argue. Typical, he would need to empty the Thai food from his body in the downstairs bathroom. Typical, she would find herself suffocating beneath a new boulder of shame and regret.

Peri sunk down in the bed, numb and dazed. She heard new footsteps sweeping into the room and then her brother was standing before her. His brown hair was a tousled bowl. No one would believe the cowlicks he was taming with all his fancy hair mousse. His face melted into relief when he saw her.

"Thank God," he said, rushing to kiss her forehead. "I was expecting to find you wrapped in bandages. The nurse made you sound much, much worse. This is the leg? They said the cut was pretty bad. Oh, my god, Peri. I think I ran over somebody's dog to get here."

Peri remained stiff. Looking up at her brother, trying to find ways to keep breathing. He looked back at her, his ocean blue eyes softening.

"I'm kidding, honey," he said. "No puppies were harmed in the making of this rescue video. Just trying to make you smile."

Her brother pouted his lip and gently pushed tendrils of hair from her face.

"Let's get you out of here," he said, spinning about to spy all of her things. "Oh! Everything's right here. This must be the guy from the fire department. The nurse said he'd been in here for a while."

Peri watched her brother examine the business card, read Lieutenant Fordham's name out loud, make a mocking face and tuck the card into his pocket. She pinned her eyes to ceiling, her heart drumming furiously against her ribcage. There was that silence again, ominous and insistent, until she heard the crackle of plastic. In her periphery, she saw her brother lift the clear garment bag from the armchair beside her bed. She felt his eyes on her, his beautiful, kind, blue eyes. Peri could not pull her own eyes from the ceiling.

Her brother chuckled. "What were you doing in Carter's shirt?"

The first brick tumbled hard from her eyes. Her shoulder jerked beneath her brother's consoling touch.

Peri felt her throat closing. The tears forcing their way free.

"Peri?" he asked, reaching to try and touch her shoulder again. The dull smack of plastic pulled her piteous eyes from the ceiling to the property bag, to his face. She disassembled into violent sobs.

Her brother's mouth puckered into a question he could not summon as she began mouthing apologies around thick cords of spittle. He tilted his head, and suddenly emptied his hands and curled them to his chest. His eyes grew wide as he staggered away from the bed, where the fish logo stared up between them.

This band, everyone says, puts on one helluva show.

DASHAFEST

It's here again, dashaFEST. What started as a single event exactly 20 years ago has evolved (exploded?) into a month-long celebration of ME.

Wait, I know how that sounds. Let me explain.

I've always enjoyed throwing parties. The theme. The games. The food and drink. Stirring around divergent circles of friends and associates inside the same venue space. I've come to feel a small tug of pride when unlikely acquaintances can trace their connections back to my living room.

Over the years, that one, overstuffed birthday party has unfolded into a whole calendar of events. A women's only event. An artistic event. A group activity. A party. Something with my daughters. Something with my immediate family. A performance showcase of some kind.

The enterprise is wholly ridiculous. I am fully aware of this. But giving myself permission to be absurd for a change is, actually, part of the appeal. For what it's worth, I'm not obnoxious about it. I don't keep tabs on who shows up and who doesn't. To be frank, I'm not concerned with guest lists at all. The events are for me. The rest of the world is simply welcome to join me. Or not.

The most spectacular element of dashaFEST, in fact, are the celebrations that happen outside of public view. Each year I challenge myself to try something new. This has landed me in opera seats, calling "pull" on a skeet shooting range, nervously waiting my turn for a colonic cleansing, and proudly brandishing my bruises after a paintball match. This year: yoga.

I also use the month to examine, fine tune and polish ME. I get real about my shortcomings, focusing intensely on one or two. (Hey, I can't fix EVERYTHING at once). I take inventory of my relationships, admitting which ones have run their course and how to better invest myself in the ones I need to keep. I am even more diligent about showing my gratitude to my family, my loved ones, my supporters, my God and myself. I am thoughtful about being THANKFUL.

I appreciate the growing number of folks who indulge —even encourage— this self-bacchanal. Friends have begun sending dashaFEST greetings as Fall approaches. One of my students said that he doesn't even think of the month as "October" any more.

Truth be told, I'd like to see more people adopt an InsertYourNameHereFEST. Have as many –or as few- parties as you want, just make sure the most important celebration is FOR you BY you. Pamper yourself. Promise yourself. Forgive yourself. Ask yourself. Check yourself. Grant yourself permission to love yourself, one designated day at a time.

It's dashaFEST everyone. Thirty-one days of being alive on purpose. I hope you'll celebrate.

WAYNE BENT *et al*

When did appetite overwhelm
your reverence for God?

The first time your tongue slid lustful
across the flash of your smile?

The last time you leaned in to hover your nose
above a sweet kindling of bargained souls?

When you sat down to gnaw through scriptures
until only the tendons of a faith remained,
you should've at least begun with grace.

MAMA THING

Kiss whimsy into my palms
Blow raspberry giggles across yummy ripples of pudge
Got sparkly magic in my fingertips
Chime bliss from thin air

Kinda fly with this
Mama Thing

Spores of future failings collect inside my worn creases
Peel back edges curled rotten from fear
Where convention and confidence fold in on themselves
Unload my best guesswork as gumption
Trust the composition

Kinda fly with this
Mama Thing

Author these moments in my own native tongue
Roll hard consonants and lilt delicate vowels
Refuse gullah patois sanctimony
Grant permission unto myself for the translation
Grant permission unto myself for the translation

Kinda fly with this
Mama Thing

Remove heavy cloaking
Bare my own misshapen wonder
Celebrate the only-est good mother I know how to be
Certified only by a quiet murmur of slumbering angels
by their tight cinch around my waist
by the vast universe blinking brightly inside their eyes

Kinda fly with this
Mama Thing

RED EYE

It happened at
the coffee shop
The collision of
a fated love
we don't yet share

I search your eyes
for alchemy magic
as you cross my body
for raw sugar
(I keep saying I'm going to
 try the brown packets, one day)

I will remember how
you bumped my elbow
Spilled your tea
Stepped back so I could reach the cream
and your chivalry could sneak a peek at my jeans

I wonder if you'll wink
If you'll say something clever
to make me smile
to introduce our lifetimes
At the coffee shop
At the gas station
Both turning our heads sideways
to read the bookshelf spines
Or maybe squeezing avocados at the market

Will our genesis burst open
trading politics at the bar
Brokering ambition at some conference
Maybe, we'll happen in the bleachers
At a stop light

Between songs
After a meeting
In the aisle of the hardware store
(I could have found the paint primer
on my own, y'know)

I lock eyes with destiny
a hundred different times a day
Logging a hundred different beginnings
to this epic, ever-after, soul-on-fire love
It could happen
It could happen
anywhere at all

Shimmer

There

Out there
Resplendent as the pyramids, the
Taj Mahal and Graceland, as
our grandmothers' wallpapered kitchens
Out there
Sit the structures of our bequeathing

Towers and icons
Archetypes and imaginings
Monuments of our gender
filling the skies with enormity and expectation

There
Out there
where the past is both distant
and fast approaching
Legacy stitches its seam between
our earth and the clouds

Here
Right here

Squinting against the slice of unforgiving sands
We point our painted toes in rank-file formation
Brave the brutal trails
between lineage and revolution
Perception and prescription
Then and now
Now and again
and again

Out there
Redemption stacks precariously

against our shared heavens
We extend calloused hands
to hold our promise in place
Offer the heft of our plush bodies to
wedge wide our glory
Solid as chapel doors

From here
We swallow honey-sweetened praise
Slide curses across our flesh
We were never told this march would be easy
We were never told to see it all the way through
We were told to set our sights on the skyline antiquity
A crowded cluster of possibilities
Chiseled hastily by the hands of men
by the hands of men
by the hands of men

From here
Our pockets weigh heavy
with lessons, scars, treasures, tools
ideas scribbled on napkins
and copper coins for casting our wishing well dreams
From here
We travel
We sway
We wander
We race
We stumble
We stop

Stop

Something glimmers along the edges
Like an oasis coaxing us to mirage waters
There
Right there
the truth of our divinity
glints boldly inside the sun

We were never told to journey beyond their horizon
We were never told to explode with our own light

Here
From right here
with star fire refracting through our bellies
We will scatter this landscape
Abandon generic paths
Follow our own shimmering horizon
to the woman
we each were beckoned to be

LAST POET OF THE SLAM

Small bubbles dance in my stomach
Excitement threatens to make me sick
Challenge me to push down and move forward

Moments like this are prayed for
but never promised, like a shooting star
screaming across the heavens

Along the mapping of my limbs
tremors are racing, nerves are shaking
Doubt cannot gain new ground

I submit my wish with both eyes open
Watched the firey tail of a miracle
blaze my hopes across the night

Dreams are held inside the knotting
of good intentions and deliberate vibrations
The universe intersecting
the eager span of my ambition

I metered my destiny in time with the cosmos
Memorized lyrics of my greatness
Pinned my name
my name
my name
against sky

This is an excerpt from my forthcoming novel,
Almost Crimson, *(Curbside Splendor Publishing, 2015).*
For release announcements or to host a local reading, please visit
http://dashakelly.com
http://curbsidesplendor.com

ALMOST CRIMSON: CHAPTER THREE

Crimson walked herself around the apartment, muttering rhyming words for the things she could name. Crimson, or CeCe, liked the way the letters sounded against each other: *couch ... ouch ... bed ... head ... key ... see ...*

Rhyming words. Mrs. Castellanos taught her The Rhyme Game, and they played in the courtyard all the time. CeCe wondered if her mother knew about rhyming words. CeCe had learned a lot of things from Mrs. Castellanos that her mother didn't know, like the Alphabet Song, Bernstein Bears, and ginger snaps. One day, CeCe had rushed inside to tell Mama about the rainbow color no one could see.

"If they can't see it, how do they know it's there?" CeCe had asked.

CeCe's mother, Carla, had sat in their kitchen with lake water eyes fixed on the table. She'd nudged her left shoulder into a weak shrug.

"They just do, CrimsonBaby," her mother said then. CeCe couldn't remember when her mother had become too weak to carry anything but tears. When the Sad started to come, pressing her mother to their bed, her Mama cried slick, silent tears for a long, long time. Longer than a game of hopscotch. Longer than singing the alphabet in her head five times. Longer than a

"just five minutes" ... never is

FB STATUS :: FEB 9 2013

nap, even. The Sad made her mother cry all the time.

CeCe wasn't big enough to pry the Sad away from her mama. Instead, she started to remember for them both. After the building manager lady fussed at Mama about their overstuffed mailbox, she remembered to pull the letters every day, even though Mama seldom opened them. When she snapped the last roll of toilet paper on its rod, CeCe remembered to pull bills with the 20s on them from the bed stand and tuck them in her shoe for her walk to the store. When CeCe could see the Baker family through their apartment window leaving in their dress-up clothes, CeCe remembered to gather Mama's underwear with hers and cover them with soap bubbles in the bathtub.

CeCe remembered to make sandwiches and open cans of fruit cocktail for lunch; she snapped rubber bands and barrettes around thick handfuls of her hair. She whisked their floor with the broom and sniffed the milk. She wiped the dishes, and she arranged her small troop of dolls into their corner each night.

CeCe's mother was slender with elfin features, with a spray of cinnamon freckles across her light brown skin. She was not an animated woman by nature, but the density of her filled the house. When her mother was filled with air and words and winking, CeCe loved the way everything about her mother would soften. There were still exceptional days, like today, when her mother tickled and ate sandwiches with her. CeCe didn't hope for those days anymore, though. Hoping made her ache on the inside of her skin.

"I think there's extra sunshine out there today," her mother said, pulling her hair into its usual ponytail. "Let's go outside to get some!"

CeCe hadn't noticed any extra sun, but she nodded in agreement anyway. She watched her mother at first. Ever since the flowers had started to push up from the ground in the courtyard, her mother's light might only last a few minutes, instead of the whole morning. Definitely not the whole day anymore. Sometimes, her mother wouldn't last for a whole game of jacks.

CeCe counted to a hundred, listening to her mother chatter while she floated about the apartment—bedroom, kitchen, bathroom, kitchen again. When she reached 101, and her mother was dressed in jeans and a button-down, CeCe allowed the giggles to spread down her elbows and knees then. She stayed smiling as her mother snapped two afro puff ponytails on the top of her head.

They decided to drag their two kitchen chairs out onto the porch slab to eat Cheerios with extra sugar. They watched the sun pull itself above the wall of their apartment complex. The residential building had been converted from a senior citizen community to low income housing the year before CeCe was born. Some of the elderly residents remained, like Mrs. Castellanos, the second-floor widow who befriended CeCe. Most of the residents were young veterans, some with wives and pre-teens, some with screaming girlfriends, and many with only bottles and brown paper bags.

The building was fashioned like an old motel, an open rectangle lined with all their front doors. CeCe had counted 24 doors on the first floor one day and 24 doors on the second floor. She knew a little something about the households behind every door. For some, she could peek past their curtained windows when she walked her imaginary pet dragon or chased a toy. Others she observed from their porch slab or the window.

CeCe didn't know most of their neighbors' names, but she recognized all of their faces. Sometimes, the grownups said hello to her when they passed, but most had learned she would only reply with a stiff wave. She would have asked their names, but they were strangers. Speaking to them wasn't allowed. Waving, on the other hand, was different.

Her feet swinging beneath her chair, CeCe scooped her cereal and listened to her mother coo about fresh starts and bright beginnings and healing wounds and buried shadows and such. CeCe didn't know what these words would look like, but her mother had been waiting for them to show up for a long time. She was about to turn up her cereal bowl and drink down the sweetened milk when her mother took the bowl from her hands and declared they were going to pick some flowers along the courtyard square.

"You walk that way, and I'll walk this way," her mother said, standing.

Between watching her mother flit along the other side of the courtyard and searching the sidewalk cracks for flowers Mama called "Danny Lions," CeCe hadn't noticed one their neighbors waving through the window. Mr. Big Mole on His Chin tapped on his window pane to get her attention. CeCe liked Mr. Big Mole. He had thick auburn sideburns, sparkly eye glasses, and the coolest bellbottom colors ever. CeCe thought there must be music playing inside his head when he walked, the way he bounced and bumped along their walkway. He didn't have children, but he did have a girlfriend who wore earrings so big, CeCe imagined them as hula hoops. CeCe saw them kissing all the time.

Mr. Big Mole had his thumbs tucked under his armpits, flapping in a funky chicken dance. CeCe burst into tickles of laughter. CeCe looked over to see if her mother was laughing too. She had rounded her second corner on the courtyard and was moving toward her daughter. Her eyes were cast to the ground, but it didn't look to CeCe like she was looking for flowers anymore. As CeCe got closer, she could see the light in her mother's face being consumed, once again, by textured shadows. When their eyes met, CeCe saw no trace of the smile that had greeted her an hour earlier.

The inside of CeCe's skin began to hurt again, and the small clutch of "Danny Lions" seemed woefully misplaced inside her hand.

"Let's go inside now, CrimsonBaby," her mother said. As CeCe took her mother's hand, she looked over her shoulder to wave goodbye to Mr. Big Mole. He waved back, but his smile and funky chicken were gone.

While CeCe placed her dandelions into a small a

Dixie cup filled with tap water, her mother retreated to their room. CeCe could hear the mattress groan its familiar embrace while she put away the kitchen step stool. CeCe brought in their chairs, rinsed and put away their cereal bowls, played with her toys, made lunch, walked her dragon, and came back inside to settle herself on the couch with one of the picture books Mrs. Castellanos had given her. CeCe fell asleep there. When she awoke from her nap, CeCe saw her mother next to her, folded into their old armchair with damp knots of tissue scattered around her like spent bullets.

CeCe said nothing, just rose from the couch to wrap her small arms around her mother's neck. Her mother didn't respond to her tight embrace. She never did. Not this version of her mother. CeCe kissed her mother's hair and went into the kitchen. She began her evening ritual of dragging one of the kitchen chairs to the fridge, reaching into the freezer for two frozen dinners, and climbing down to spin the oven dial to 4-2-5. Pushing the chair back to the table, CeCe noticed tufts of yellow winking at her from the garbage can. CeCe's skinned ached again. There was their sunshine morning, tossed in the trash.

Sitting at the table, CeCe finished her dinner while her mother picked absently at the plate compartments. Her mother had begun eating less and less.

"Why were you sad today, Mama?"

"I just am, CrimsonBaby. I just am."

Let's raise our sons. Stronger. Educate our daughters. Better. Lift expectations. Higher. Convict careless language. Together. Let's call rape, RAPE. Always. Even if he's a football star. Even if he's fine. Even if he shared his family name. Even if there was booze and dope and glimpses of flesh. It's rape, even then. Reshaping our "rape culture" demands that we each own and alter our small parts of complicity, our turning of heads, our easy dismissal and judgment, our uneasy laughter at boys-will-be-boys offenses, our loud volume head bobbing to misogyny music, our unspoken insistence that men are clumsy hunters and video-sorority-party-girl-vixens are their prey (I mean, all he wants for his birthday is a big booty girl, right?) Steubenville is happening everywhere, everyday. America's relationship with its women MUST be stronger, better, higher, together, always.

FB STATUS :: MARCH 20 2013

I'm traveling from an all-girls' high school to an all-women's correctional facility. There's a poem in there somewhere...

FB STATUS :: NOV 18 2009

I would like to quickly review the rules for laying down baby hair, applying black lip liner and drawing eyebrows: Don't.

FB STATUS :: MAY 15 2009

I would like -very much- to put the rest of my daughters' curves on layaway. Really.

FB STATUS :: OCT 8 2010

SOMEONE LIKE YOU

A hate to turn up out of the blue uninvited
But I couldn't stay away, couldn't fight it
I had hoped you'd see my face
and that you'd be reminded that for me, it isn't over
                                                                            ~Adele

I've written enough love notes
and broken-hearted poems to know that
this was something different
Not because I pulled the loose leaf sheet
from beneath the fold of his daily news and
Not because the handwriting was lilted and faint and
Not because her language was weighted
with words like forever and love and we but
because of the howling trapped
between the paper and the ink

Heartbreak familiar scaled her edges of upper cases
I appraised the downward slope of her consonants
to be the hieroglyphs of we women who
tend to love like mountain molasses
Thick, sweet, steady
Without prompting
Without apology
Without stopping
Our scars meter distances between
left and lost
dropped and broken

I hear echoes
of light laughter behind her fluid pen
Imagine what they were like, when
my man loved her then
Back before he laced sure fingers with mine
Back when his thumb traced

the landscape of her spine
Back when they were building their own lexicon with
every inside joke and whispered exchange
Back when they had a favorite diner, and he forgave
her picking French fries from his plate

I imagine her cheeks flushed warm from adoring him
Eyes shiny in feverish affection and
I bet she believed in forever then
Bet she wrapped old wounds
with plush stretches of him

Back when he loved her back, I bet
he called her pet names
Surprised her at work with
lunch on some days
I know he touched her gently
Planting sweet fruits along her wrists and collarbone

I also know the smell of souring affection
Remember scouring my own heart raw
to rise from my own rubble and
fall into his refreshed embrace

I wonder if a beast still lurks behind his chest

Will it ever come for me
Ever rage me away from my bones
I suppose my own skeletons dance
elegantly now with new loves
Better loves, like this man of hers
repurposed into my bed
I've nestled his history beneath my skin
Together, we dream with the precision of planets
But he loved her
something different
Something fractured, something
stretched insufficient

between devotion and farewell
She will always remember him this way

I fold the letter back into its hiding place

Her loss, my gain
Her closure, my praise
I don't know where this
beginning might lead,
but I pray we can love any ending
something
Different

INCANTATION No. 4

Keep me.
Nestle my core
into the mass of your hand
Wrist locked steady
Careful now
Careful now
Don't cradle me
bird's nest suspended
Canopy me with fleshy fingers
Keep me.

Thread yourself through all the letters
of all my names
Especially those you whisper
over me when I sleep
(you *do* watch me when I sleep, don't you?)
Loop my alphabet around your neck
Careful now
Careful now
Don't flaunt me
bauble shiny
Drape my charms closer to your chest than
the world
Keep me.

Tuck my affections
in the pocket of your jeans
Slip me deep in cotton corners
weightless and constant
Careful now
Careful now
Don't stroke absently
at smooth surfaces
Carry my devotion,
reaching in to trace firm contours as needed

Keep me.
Talisman true

Keep me
Keep me
with you.

Maximus

Hips gear
Arms swing
Lungs hum with breath music

Muscles clench
in earnest
in turn

Adductors
Hamstrings
Quads
Engine me ahead
toward home
toward silhouette goal

The Gluteus, she toggles
Keeps time with the march
She is uninvolved, but invested
Their contractions are her gain

So she accompanies us each morning
Upright on her palanquin carriage
Leaving us to our labor
as she waves regally
to traffic passing by

SPOONING

Breathe rhythm and warmth
into my hair
onto my neck

Loop your arms
inside and around
Lock your angles
into my curves

The sturdy truth of you
aligns with mine
From head to toe
we rest, we relent

A new sun yearns
against our window

Love teaching children!! ...uh...wait... that one over there in the blue? Not so much.

I see the problem now ... you've got me confused with an average woman. Yeah, your bad ...

I'm in the fast lane of Yellow Brick Road

Dude: I'm sure you're over 21, but the cops have been giving everybody a hard time lately.
Me: No problem. *digs in wallet for license*
Dude: Damn!! Me: Uh, thanks? Dude: Hell yeah...!
Me: *grinning as I sashay away* #circa1969

SAM

I teach at a writing camp for middle school students in the summer. Boys. Girls. Black. White. City. Outskirts. Comfortable. Underserved. All enamored with the sparks of magic between their pens and lined paper.

For the past three summers, Samantha has been one of the half dozen perennial students in the class. My first year, Sam's name was one that I never forgot. Partly, because I've always thought boys' names on girls was super cool. Mostly, though, it was her satirical humor and irrepressible spunk. Small enough to fold herself in two between the table edge and plastic chairs, the small knots of her knees peeking above her composition notebook. Above those pages, her brown hair dipped into a voluminous bob just above her ears and her large, dark eyes.

Sam was excited to share the industry happening inside her head, always asking questions to carve permissions for some outlying idea. She talked fast too, with her S's leaking through the sides of her smile. I recognized right away that the flare she kept sending up was saying to me *I'm smarter than your average bear cub.*

Indeed, she was.

Still is.

Sam's writing is still clever and deliberate, now matured with a dimension of subtlety. This summer, however, I was not fixated with her ideas or metaphors. This year, my attention was wholly seized by the bobby pin in her hair.

"Is that a *bobby pin* in Sam's hair?" I asked the camp director. She looked and nodded. And so it begins, our satisfied smiles agreed.

After three summers together, basic biology certainly dictated the elongated limbs, the stretching height and rounded brassiere. But *this* was a bobby pin, and it came to camp with Sam everyday to hold that new panel of hair into place above her eye.

Her spirit was still wonderfully irreverent, even though she was less assertive than summers past. Her sense of fashion was still stitched in counter culture, although the belt buckles, hoodies and bracelets seemed placed with more strategy. She still reads aloud at lightening speed, but her hand does not thrust anxiously into the air these days. That hand, instead, was occupied with her new hair, tracing the contours and twisting the straightened brown length around her fingers. I imagined numerous hours in front of a mirror with that bobby pin and fistfuls of hair.

Once I adjusted to the shock, I took note of how aware she seemed to be with this new girlified version of herself. I wonder if she has embraced this new moon, or if its afterglow is engulfing her unaware. Maybe this nascent femininity washed over her in indecipherable degrees. Maybe her bathroom mirror doesn't articulate the softening of features and delicate curvatures in her face. Maybe she's already lost count of the times her fingers have raked through her hair or adjusted her sk8tergirl tee.

Sam is distinctly pretty now. I wonder if she sees that. I stumbled awkwardly over each seemingly abrupt new terrain of woman: training bras, mascara, sanitary pads, shaving, exchanging phone numbers, gossip, perfume, endless investments into nail and hair products and earrings that dangled. The milestones were easy compared to the nuances waiting for me between young girl and young woman. Had I rolled those pop rock moments across my tongue, delighting in my own mini bursts of newness, I'm confident that my arrival into womanhood would have felt less like a crash landing.

Fairly confident.

I can see, now, how getting lost in the fingering of curls or renegotiating the mechanics of long, heavy limbs would have helped me actually exist through my transformation, not simply emerge disoriented from the butterfly process.

I'm wishing this for Sam right now. More than crisp

stanzas or plot arcs, I hope Sam feels the thin wings that are yawning open behind her. I hope she's stamping permanent memories with every new marking. I hope she hears the young woman inside preparing to take flight and dance metaphors into the wind.

Dancing, with a bobby pin in her hair.

Getting a stern talking to from God.
All love, all good, all grace, glory
and stuff ... but He ain't playin.'

FB STATUS :: AUG 5 2010

peers curiously into my hat
"Hello, Rabbit? Hello..?"

FB STATUS :: MARCH 10 2009

Pigs will not fly. Not even with counseling. Or
coaching. Or fancy new clothes. Or affirmations. Or
cuddling. Or the last bite of your sandwich. It is not
for lack of focus. Or prejudice or profiling. Or being
tied up on the phone. Or having a broken heart. Or
having things easy. Or some withering away of faith.
It is because they are pigs. At best, they may hang
weightless for a moment, defy gravity for a moment,
suspend our understanding of hard earth and
crushing impact ... for a moment. At the end of it all,
we will remember how this truth had always been
wedged inside the marrow of our bones. Pigs.
They will not. Fly.

STATUS :: JULY 1 2013

bbpft! ppbt! pppbbbt! pphfft! bppbsshpt!!
wipes spittle, makes face
Yuck ...almost got that Doubt in my mouth

FB STATUS :: JAN 22 2014

CALL IT FORTH

Hunger
Desire
Crave
Dream
Taste
Imagine
Call it forth

Wrestle
Split
Claw
Release
Scar
Insist
Call it forth

Measure
Scout
Construct
Manifest
Invent
Call it forth

Conjure
Command
Affirm
Ignite
Seize permissions from the stars
Claim your everything, divined and due

Speak future truth with ancient convictions
Call it forth
Call it forth
Call it forth

You

Thank you for choosing my words! I hope you were moved in some way by this collection.

This doesn't have to be the end.

If you enjoyed CALL IT FORTH, please consider introducing me and my words to your city. As a facilitator, teaching artist and performer. I apply my craft and the science of the creative process to lead workshops and discussions on creativity, team building and personal exploration. I would welcome the opportunity to share my words and work with your organization or community.

While I'm being forward and asking for favors...

Please consider sharing feedback about your experience with Call It Forth. Your power words give me energy and encouragement! They also help connect the wide world of readers and communities supporting this project. You can post comments on any of these social media stations:

> Facebook—CALL IT FORTH or Dasha Kelly
> Twitter—Dasha Kelly
> Instagram—Dasha_Kelly
> Website—http://dashakelly.com

Again, thank you! I wish you many blessings and hope you've been inspired to also CALL IT FORTH...

DASHA KELLY is a nationally
-respected writer, artist and
social entrepreneur. She travels
extensively as a performer,
speaker and facilitator. She has
been invited to college campuses,
board rooms, professional con-
ferences, K-12 classrooms,
teacher in-services, group homes,
churches, correctional institu-
tions, arts programs, senior cen-
ters, healing retreats and a living
room or two.

Dasha has performed throughout the U.S. and
abroad. She appeared on the final season of *HBO presents
Russell Simmons' Def Poetry Jam* and has shared stages
with UK's Linton Kwesi Johnson, former U.S. poet laureate
Elizabeth Alexander, Wisconsin poet laureate Max Gar-
land, Grammy-nominated Angie Stone, classical composer
Liza White, and comedians Tommy Davidson and Damon
Williams. She appeared in the indie film *Role Play* and the
documentary *Mark My Words*. In 2014, Dasha traveled to
Botswana as an Arts Envoy for the U.S. Embassy.

She's published a novel, *All Fall Down,* (Syntax,
2003); a collection of work, *Hershey Eats Peanuts*
(Penmanship Books, 2009); written for several magazines, to include *Upscale, Black Enterprise* and *Milwaukee*;
and is included in several anthologies. Her second novel,
Almost Crimson, will be available through Curbside Splendor Publishing in 2015.

Dasha holds an MFA in Creative Writing from An-
tioch University. She is a former writer-in-residence for
the historic Pfister Hotel and an alum of the iconic Squaw
Valley Writers Community. Dasha is also founder of Still
Waters Collective, an arts education and community-
building initiative.

A former "Army brat," Dasha is currently based out
of Milwaukee, where she lives with her cat and two teen
daughters.